C000176096

REITH

REITH

THE B.B.C YEARS

BY

ROGER MILNER

MAINSTREAM
PUBLISHING

Copyright © Roger Milner, 1983
All rights reserved.

First published in 1983 by
MAINSTREAM PUBLISHING COMPANY (EDINBURGH) LTD.
25 South-West Thistle Street Lane
EDINBURGH EH2 1EW

ISBN 0 906391 43 1

No part of this book may be reproduced or transmitted in any
form or by any means without permission in writing from the
publisher, except by a reviewer who wishes to quote brief
passages in connection with a review written for insertion in
a magazine, newspaper or broadcast.

All photographs used from the dramatisation REITH in this book
are copyright of BBC Enterprises Limited. All other photographs
used—with the exception of the Bowser family photograph which
was kindly loaned by the Bowser family—were obtained from the
B.B.C. Written Archives Centre at Caversham Park, Reading.

Cover design by WEEF.

Typeset by Spectrum Printing Company, Edinburgh.
Printed and bound by Billing & Sons Limited, Worcester.

Author's Note

REITH: THE BBC YEARS has been largely culled from the extensive personal diaries of Lord Reith. Events and people are seen through his eyes without comment or hindsight—except his own (the diaries were amended throughout his life).

I have been greatly helped by Miss Jo Stanley, who was not only Reith's Private Secretary for many years, but also a friend of the family. Christopher Reith and his sister Marista Leishman, Lord Reith's children, have allowed me complete access to their father's papers and assisted in every way possible. I am also grateful to other relatives and friends, and to the many former workers of the B.B.C. who wrote to me out the blue. Their letters all pay tribute to the man who founded that great organisation.

REITH: THE B.B.C. YEARS is a direct result of my dramatisation of *REITH* for B.B.C.-T.V., first broadcast in November 1983. Tom Fleming played Reith for that dramatisation, while the role of Muriel was played by Dinah Stabb. Others in the cast included Joyce Carey, Jan Carey, Charles Hathorn, Davina Sullivan, Marion Owen-Smith, Brian Miller, Hermione Gregory, Malcolm Stoppard, David Quilter, Jeffry Wickham, James Grout, Clifford Parrish, Robert Lang, Peter Barkworth, Julia Hills, Juliette Mole, Mona Bruce, John Cording, Jim Norton, Frank Mills, Sebastian Shaw, Christopher Reilly, Edward Lyon, Rita Davies, as well as many supporting artists. Innes Lloyd and Alan Sleath have been particularly supportive of my efforts with regard to both the dramatisation and the book.

Finally, my thanks go to the B.B.C. Archives at Caversham Park, Reading. They are still typing out the later volumes of the diaries. Reith estimated them at four-and-a-half million words, so if anybody else wants to learn more about John Reith I can safely echo the profound words of the Scotsman when a lady admired his kilt—"Aye. And there's yards and yards mair where that came from."

Roger Milner
September, 1983

To Innes

1

The war was over and the decorations were doled out. John Reith took one look at his 1914-18 ribbon and tore it up. It was the same as the ribbon for the Somme Battle in which he'd been wounded. He was disgusted. He'd been in the army for the whole war, and all he'd got at the end of it was the same bit of ribbon as everyone else.

Having reacted so melodramatically, he looked around his old bedroom at the Manse to see if there'd been any reaction. None. But he could hear his sister Jean complaining loudly to his mother about lack of money. He objected to the way Jean lived on the old couple and made them miserable. The noise was louder—had she no consideration for anyone?

He went down to see his father, propped up in bed. He was asleep, frail and helpless. John stood for a moment looking at him, remembering the robust and visionary clergyman who had guided him throughout his life, and now could guide him no more—except in general terms of duty and service and love of God. He felt a sudden anger. But it was useless, unproductive anger, the same anger that had come over him when he rushed round Glasgow clutching a heavy spanner, determined to brain the van driver who'd run over his father. The anger melted away. His father was slowly dying—in a year, maybe two. He knew it wasn't the accident, it was cancer.

Jean ran up to her bedroom and slammed the door. A woman of thirty-eight still behaving like a schoolgirl.

It was a crisp afternoon—he'd go up to the monument—it wouldn't take long—he'd be back for tea. He closed the door noiselessly and let himself out of the house. Tomorrow he'd catch the sleeper and be back in Shoreham. He had to decide what was to be done. The monument would tell him, like the Oracle at Delphi.

Once there, he stood, getting his breath, looking at the mist giving Glasgow back its youth and innocence. Just the odd high chimney to remind him of the docks and slums and coughing and spitting humanity. The sun was warm and he sat down, his long legs scooped up under his chin. How many times had he sat thus? He remembered his nursemaid who'd forced him to sit like the monument itself for hours while she and her boyfriend held hands and talked. She'd done him a great service—the monument was his place now, his place apart. Of course he liked going to church and would often pray earnestly for reassurance and guidance, and for those he loved. He didn't often give thanks to the Almighty, that was not part of the bargain. He would inform God that he trusted him and would try not to let him down, and in consequence expected God to reciprocate in full measure by providing whatever was required urgently. But at the monument he was untrammeled by religion and his father's teachings. He was out in the open. If God appeared he'd have to come out of the fiery bush with a voice like thunder.

He relaxed and let the sun lick his wounds. The wounded face, with the deep hollow where the bullet struck him, the wounded mind which never stopped its crippling search for glory, and the wounded heart which from childhood days had longed for a hand to cling to, a shoulder to lean on, a soothing voice to whisper approval and understanding. Yet that same hand must never cling to his, and the voice must remain silent when requested.

He took out his notebook and wrote down the questions that had to be answered before he went back down to the Manse. Firstly—How soon would he be demobbed? Secondly—What should he do once he was demobbed? And third—Where should he live at Shoreham?

He didn't spend long thinking about the first two questions. He couldn't answer either—it wasn't up to him. Presumably the Admiralty would keep him till most of the vast accumulation of war machinery was disposed of. As for the future—everything

was changing so rapidly, who knows what job might be offered
him? He only knew that he wanted to be in the Cabinet in five
years, or ten at the most. The ladders to high office were various.
He could seek his fortune in the Empire, or return to the U.S.A.
where he'd made many friends while organising munitions, or
he could become an M.P. He was sure about one thing—he
wan't going back to civil engineering in the bowels of Scottish
Industry.

Number 3—where should he live for the next six months?
That question he could answer. He'd had enough of digs and
Brighton landladies. Now that the war was over they too wanted
to get back to normal, and were thinking of the coming summer
when their rooms—like the commandeered hotels at the front—
would once more be full of visitors and children and sand in the
hall and buckets and spades. He didn't want to be part of that
metamorphosis, with landladies rising from the pier like the
Botticelli Venus. Even when out of the line in 1915, he'd always
tried to find himself an exclusive billet away from the mess. He
didn't care for his brother officers then, and he didn't care for
them now. He wanted a small house or bungalow where he
could be "cosy" with his own things round him. Nothing grand
or luxurious.

"That's all I want," he said out loud. "And that's all Charlie
wants."

The Oracle had spoken.

Charlie was at the station to meet his train. They embraced
warmly and took a taxi to their digs. John explained "the plan"
and they went to look at a bungalow the same afternoon, took it,
and moved in at the weekend. John had to get his C.O.'s
permission first, but it was a mere formality. Colonel Thompson
was hoping to be demobbed and was busy looking round for a
wife. He had his eye on John's driver, Miss Odhams, so it paid to
be on good terms with his second-in-command. John happily
gave advice and counsel without knowing the first thing about
the Colonel and his love life, though he did wonder at the
Colonel's deep religiosity which prevented him from declaring
himself to Miss Odhams for fear he wasn't good enough.

"He means he doesn't think *she's* good enough!" said Charlie.

Life at Shoreham was for John rather as he imagined life might be at the university. There was, of course, no academic curriculum, but he had a sense of liberation and exposure. He'd longed to go to university like his elder brothers but his father couldn't afford to rear more than two clergymen, and had forced John into engineering. So his five to nine existence (5a.m. to 9p.m.) had taken him from a raw youth of eighteen to a man of twenty-five and the war had deprived him of any natural flowering. Now he was thirty.

"I may be a giant physically," he told his mother, "but mentally my growth has been stunted."

His mother, ever unwilling to prefer the Benjamin of the family to the others, only smiled and patted his hand. Her intense loyalty to her husband made it impossible for her to take John's side, and without such help, the young adolescent had to do as he was told without further questioning.

But his father was a spent force, and John was able to, if not taste, at least reach up and touch the forbidden fruit. For one thing, for the first time in his life he was in almost daily contact with a young and attractive woman, Miss Odhams, his driver. At first he had hardly noticed her, regarding her as part of the old Sunbeam she chauffeured. But the Colonel's predicament made him examine her with greater interest, to see if he could resolve the Colonel's problem. She was obviously young and pretty, with nice eyes and a soft and gentle smile—so she must have a sense of humour—but she seemed rather shy. Perhaps that was because he was her Boss and she couldn't answer back if she wanted to.

"Have you any idea how old she is?" he asked Charlie suddenly.

"How old who is?"

"Miss Odhams, my driver?"

"Between twenty and thirty."

"Between twenty and thirty—is that a fact?" John nodded his head as though confirming some inner calculation.

"Why do you ask?" Charlie was amused at his friend's evident interest in his driver.

"Thompson is thinking of her as a possible wife. Don't mention it to her, by the way."

"As though I would."

Charlie was shoving his rugger clothes into a bag.

"Have you seen my shorts?"

"Probably in the kitchen—Mrs Logan did some washing."

Charlie found them.

"Are you coming to watch?"

"Who are you playing?"

"United Services."

"I might—on the other hand I might not. Good luck anyway. Be back by six—we're going to see a film."

"Are we? Oh good."

Charlie went off cheerfully. He accepted John's wishes without question. If John had said, "We'll go for a swim" or "We'll walk along the beach" or "Go out to dinner" or even "Go to London or Scotland or . . .", well, "Timbuktoo", he'd almost certainly have agreed without demur. He might have had second thoughts later, particularly if he'd mentioned the subject to his mother. Mrs Bowser disapproved of John's influence over her son. It was a natural mother's instinct. Charlie was barely out of his teens, and John Reith was a mature man of thirty. She didn't deny that John had helped her son in many ways. When John had first met him, Charlie had been a schoolboy without a thought in his head. But he'd blossomed into a clever and spirited young man, good at almost everything. Under John's tutelage, he had learned to concentrate his talents on one thing at a time, to become master of his subject before making the next move—be it disposing of a dozen old army trucks, or kicking a penalty goal. Above all, John had imparted to him his own deep religious convictions, his love of the Bible, and delight in the Scottish hymns and psalms which had been so much a part of his own upbringing. Mrs Bowser admitted that in many respects John had been the making of her boy and was grudgingly grateful. But he was still her "wee bairn", and she was jealous of the man who had stolen that child from her.

John was almost totally unaware of how others saw him. If he paused to reflect at all—which he rarely did—he would reflect

upon the failings of others, not his own. Mrs Bowser was a
clucking mother hen, worrying about a chick that had left the
nest. She had no business to worry. Charlie had got a wonderful
job as John's assistant and had been highly commended by a
visiting Brigadier. What more could she ask? The fact that he'd
got Charlie the job in the first place, and that the job had taken
the ewe lamb away from home was, to John's way of thinking, all
to the good.

John went to watch the match, as he knew he would. He
himself had played when at the Glasgow Academy and later at
Greshams. He'd been keen, but he was really too tall for comfort.
At sixteen he'd been six-foot-four and still growing. He couldn't
play any more. One kick on the side of his head, and his mouth
would be full of gold fillings and broken bits of teeth. He still
had to make regular visits to the dentist to repair the damage
from the sniper's solitary bullet which nearly cost him his life.
He rubbed his gum, and the next moment was on his feet
cheering his friend wildly as he raced down the wing to score a
try. There weren't more than a handful of spectators, and John
made more noise than the lot of them. But he was unaware of
them. He was like a racehorse owner with only one horse in the
stable—his heart was bursting to win, but not for himself—for
Charlie his pupil, his friend and soulmate . . . Charlie.

Later they went to the cinema and saw Chaplin's latest. John
thought him very funny, and Charlie laughed so much John
thought he'd burst a blood vessel.

The next afternoon they went for a drive with Miss Odhams
and the Colonel and two sisters—one for John and the other for
Charlie. John sat down with Christine and looked at the sea and
talked about *The Ancient Mariner* which he'd been reading to
Charlie. Christine said she was cold and snuggled up to him.
John paused in the midst of his dissertation on the wingspan of
the albatross , and asked her if she'd like to kiss him. He knew
the albatross, and asked her if she'd like to kiss him. He knew
she wanted to, but he didn't. When she didn't reply he explained
he'd no experience). There were welcoming kisses, and farewell
kisses, and holy kisses, and the kiss of Judas . . . Christine got up
and ran to catch up the others. She was only eighteen and as far

as she was concerned a kiss was just for fun.

But he got a Christmas card from her a few days later. He put it with the others on the mantelpiece for Charlie to see. It had lots of kisses and hugs under the signature, and a P.S. scrawled across a red-faced Father Christmas—"I'm dying to kiss you!" Charlie laughed and showed him one from the other sister saying, "Kiss me again!" They saw the girls around, but never went for another walk with them. The weather had turned cold anyway and they had to go home for Christmas.

The Manse was decorated. Mrs Reith was English and Christmas was the only time she hoisted the Red Cross of St. George. But it was an empty gesture—there was little joy with her husband weakening every day, unable even to attend a service, let alone conduct one. Robert looked in on them to collect whatever presents he could lay his hands on, and Jean was very weepy. Her husband had been home from three weeks with his parents, and she'd never even been asked round. She got no sympathy from John. He was angry because he'd paid for the installation of electricity on the ground floor, and Jean had had it put into her bedroom as well.

"He's going straight back to India, Jean." He'd met him on the station. "He wants to forget you ever happened."

Jean finished her piece of Christmas cake, and then left the room.

"You shouldn't have said that, John," said his mother.

"Why not? It's true."

"Because a thing's true doesn't mean you have to say it out loud to Jean. She's very hurt."

"So am I. She never even said 'Thank you' for the handbag and scarf I gave her."

His mother patted his hand. She knew how much trouble he always went to to buy Christmas presents for all the family. She'd had an enormous bunch of flowers, two books and a suitcase. "The Hendersons have asked you round on New Year's Eve," she told him. "Maisie was asking after you."

He knew Maisie and didn't think much of her. But it was common talk that she'd inherit 1500 acres and £20,000 when she was twenty-one.

"I saw her at Communion this morning. I told her I couldn't come."

"Oh, why not, dear?"

"I've got to get back to Shoreham by the 30th. I've promised to see the New Year in with Charlie."

"Oh, very well." Mrs Reith knew it was no good arguing if Charlie was involved. "Will you take this piece of cake in to Father? He was asking to see you."

He took the cake to his father who ate a tiny piece of the icing.

"Have you thought about getting married, John?"

"Yes, father, but not much."

"You must want to have a house of your own." He sipped his tea. "And someone to care for you and bring you a cup of tea."

"Oh yes, I want that."

When he got back to the bungalow, he told Charlie what his father had said. He always told Charlie everything and vice-versa. That was part of the secret of their friendship—they had no secrets from each other. Charlie said nothing, but got up and went into the kitchen and a moment later brought him a mug of tea.

"Here you are. You don't need to get forced into marriage just yet."

They went over to the Mess later, but didn't stay. There'd be plenty of beer-swilling sergeants invited in with their wives to bring in the New Year. John and Charlie preferred to sit in front of their own good fire and chat and let 1918 slide away unnoticed and unregretted.

For Charlie the war had seemed part of his life. Four years at school—one of his friends who was only three months older than him had been killed on November 2nd. But Charlie didn't feel lucky to be alive. He thought his school friend was very unlucky to be dead—a week before it all ended. And he had no romantic illusions about getting into action. John had seen to that. He'd given Charlie his war diary to read in 1916 before he went to America. "Stay in the O.T.C., Charlieboy, where it's fun and the bullets have no lead in them." And Charlie had promised not to volunteer early, but to wait till he was called up.

"We'll see the New Year in with a drop of whisky, Charlie."—
He'd kept a bottle hidden. Charlie liked a drop of Scotch. "And
I'll smoke a cigarette too in your honour!"

That was one bad habit Charlie'd got him into. At least that's
what he said, but he admitted that it was a bad habit he really
enjoyed. But to have a drink except on high days and holidays
was almost a sin. He'd seen enough of the poverty and misery of
the back streets of Glasgow. The men he'd worked with as an
engineer were the élite—craftsmen, solid citizens—like the
sergeants and corporals they became. But the Glaswegian Jock in
the trenches had gone back to the Gorbals still uneducated,
unloved and unrewarded. Forgotten the moment their medals
had been distributed. John had met some of them over
Christmas. He'd told them the date of the reunion and they'd
promised to attend. That was one way he could help them. He'd
make sure he did.

"It's nearly midnight," said Charlie. They could hear a church
clock beginning to chime.

They stood up and raised their glasses in silence.

"Not till the last stroke," said John.

Charlie looked across at his friend. John was always so
meticulous about celebrating an event. Birthdays, weddings,
funerals, and the New Year. Mrs Bowser had wanted her son to
stay and see the New Year in with them. She was very upset
when he refused, and burst into tears.

"You seem only to be happy with John. This is your home!"

But this bungalow in Brighton was his home and the war was
over.

John was sniffing the whisky appreciatively. The church clock
began to strike midnight. They could hear other bells being
rung—all the clocks in Brighton were chiming. But they let their
own church take them into 1919, a New Year untouched and
untarnished, like their friendship.

2

John enjoyed his job. Having spent the best part of a year in the U.S.A. securing the much-needed supplies for the front, he knew how to deal with the problems of manufacture and dispersal. But he instinctively cut corners and red tape. In America this was expected and welcomed, but in Britain both during and after the war, such flagrant unorthodoxy was .often resented by senior officers. Fortunately Colonel Thompson, whatever his other failings in John's eyes, was only too glad to get the work done. He quickly appreciated that providing he left John to get on with it in his own way—which included having Charles Bowser as assistant —he need never worry. John, for his part, had learned a little of how to deal with his seniors. He made sure he asked for their opinion first, before ignoring it. He remembered the Colonel who had given him three weeks to find suitable sites for supply dumps in the war. He told John he had three weeks. John reappeared three days later with a complete report and recommendation. "All I did was ring up the local police stations and get them to suggest suitable places. Then I went down and drove round," he wrote to Charlie. But the C.O. was not at all pleased, because it meant he had to look around for some other job to keep the office going.

Europe in 1919 was a mess as far as John could see. He wished he was in charge. Moreover, at the rate he was going at Shoreham, in six months time there'd be no more stuff to dispose of. A visiting War Office wallah had actually complimented him, so John had hinted that he would welcome some sort of similar work when he got demobbed—somewhere abroad perhaps? The Wallah had mentioned Serbia.

"Ever been to Serbia?"

"No, sir."

"No end of equipment out there—Italian, German, all sorts. Do you speak any languages?"

"German and Italian and French. I daresay I could manage Serbo Croat if I had to," he said without hesitation.

"Well, I'll put your name forward."

It sounded promising. Meanwhile . . . he enjoyed his life at Shoreham and made the most of it. Particularly the Sunbeam motor car. He wasn't much of a driver himself, so he sat back contentedly and let Miss Odhams steer and change gears. She was not allowed to go for long, however, without being given directions—"Turn left, turn right—there's a nasty bend coming up—slow down, overtake, put your foot on the brake . . ." Miss Odhams objected strongly to his endless instructions, and said so very politely on several occasions. Eventually, Charlie persuaded him to leave the driving to his chauffeur and look at the view.

John admired the view and then began to look at Miss Odhams, and after a time admired her as well. It was a gradual awakening on John's part—prompted, of course, by Colonel Thompson's reluctant courtship of Muriel, Miss Odham's other name.

"How are you getting on with Miss Odhams?" Charlie asked him after she'd met them at Brighton Station and dropped them at the bungalow.

"How are you?" asked John, hedging.

"I like her very much—she's a nice girl."

"Too good for Thompson, and that's a fact."

They returned to the subject after supper. They'd both been in London for the weekend—John to see his brother Douglas off to Clunie, where he was assisting at the Cathedral, a job not worthy of his talents, as John had informed him. Douglas and Ada didn't complain, they were only too glad to have a roof over their heads after missionising in Africa.

"Mother was complaining about our friendship," said Charlie.

"What's it got to do with her?"

"Nothing, but . . ."

Charlie tried to put his parents' point of view, while John
talked glowingly of the benefits of their friendship, and intensity
of it, the sense of well-being and happiness and sharing. "And I
don't mean just sharing our lives as we're leading them now, I
mean sharing our future. We've neither of us been placed on this
earth to follow some humdrum well-trodden path to non-
existence. We're destined for something great."

"I know you are, John, but . . ."

"And so are you, Charlieboy. You heard what the Brigadier
said—he was confident and comforted by the way you've
handled things when the Colonel was away. Mind you, it took a
bit to make him swallow the way I've been selling the stuff off
without consulting the Treasury!"

"I can see you'll be an M.P. in a year or two, John."

"The Cabinet or nothing."

"Yes. But I'm not so ambitious as you—I should be quite
content to live in Scotland and have a farm or something."

"I hear you," said John—his way of winding up an unpleasant
conversation.

"No, you don't, Johnnie. I want to get married."

"You want to . . . ?" John was astounded. "Who to?"

"I don't know."

"You can't say you want to get married if you haven't got a girl
in mind."

"Why not? When I say I want to get married, I mean I want to
get married."

"All right," said John. "You want to get married. When?"

"When . . . I find the right girl."

"And you haven't anybody in mind?"

"No."

"Charlie—you remember what I was saying about our friendship and how much I valued it?"

"Yes."

"Well, what I didn't say is that it's not been achieved without
sacrifice. I've had several good chances at marriage already.
Good chances. Do you know there are two girls walking about
Glasgow now to whom I could be married if I'd lifted my little
finger?" He paused for effect. "They're both worth two million,

what's more."

"Where are they?" Charlie leapt up and looked round the room.

John didn't laugh.

"They're married to someone else. One of them to a man old enough to be her father." He said this decisively, as though that proved his point that Charlie should remain single until further notice. But Charlie was unconvinced and said so.

So now John had both the Colonel and Charlie in a state of "marriage flux". Or was it Spring Fever? Sex was not something that he'd ever heard mentioned at the Manse—except by Jean in a moment of hysteria. And Beth, his favourite sister, had once complained that the whole Presbyterian ethos was stifling her and frustrating her, and she was going to get out. And she did and went off nursing, and when he had asked her what she saw in some doctor she was carrying on with she'd said, "Sex." Certainly sex came into marriage, but you had to meet a girl first and fall in love, and neither Charlie nor the Colonel showed the remotest signs of being in love. The Colonel might be, but Charlie certainly wasn't. He hadn't got a girlfriend to start with . .

Nevertheless, the whole thing couldn't be dismissed as a passing fad. Charlie had obviously meant what he said about wanting to get married, and the Colonel was seriously on the look-out for someone worthy to share his life. John concluded that what they wanted was a wife, which was something very different. Yes, a wife. And a wife, unlike a passionate love affair, could be sought out and secured. He would see what could be done for Charlie—the Colonel must do his own dirty work.

As for himself . . . John was a romantic. He must find his true love and marry her and live happily ever after.

The warm weather may have awakened sexual desires in the Colonel and Charlie, in John the Spring Tides brought a desire for long walks. Long walks had taken him all over Scotland. He had only to see a hill at the back of wherever he was to want to rush up it and down again in record time. He stopped long enough on the summit to take in the view and commune with the Almighty, then it was off down the slopes with great long

strides. The proximity of the hills round Brighton urged him on.
And with him—Charlie. And as he had a beautiful motor car at
his disposal, they naturally drove, and as the car was driven, by
Miss Odhams—now called Muriel when he remembered—and
she liked walks, or said she did, John and Charlie and Muriel
made frequent excursions around Brighton.

On the first occasion John looked up a route on a map, but got
lost, and was heading off cross-country when Muriel called after
him: "Major Reith—you're going in the opposite direction!"

He stopped and turned round. "We came here with the sun
behind us," he said, rejoining her. "Now we've got the sun in our
eyes. How can I be going in the wrong direction?"

"Brighton's over there, I promise you." She pointed south. "You
can see the sea."

"Balderdash!" said John.

"It's not balderdash. I live near here, and I've been this way
dozens of times. That's the sea—isn't it Charles?"

Charles agreed.

"All right," said John, and they turned back. "And by the way,
Miss Odhams, if you're going to call Mr Bowser Charles, you can
call me John."

"Yes, sir," she said, and smiled at Charlie.

"But not in the office mind," John added.

"No, sir."

From then on it was Major Reith and Miss Odhams in the
office, but John and Muriel on their expeditions, which became a
twice-weekly occurrence. And still John didn't know how old she
was. He asked Charlie while they were having breakfast one day.

"I don't know. Why not ask the Thompson?"

"Oh, I couldn't do that. He'll think I'm after his girl."

Charlie didn't say anything more. But it was obvious what he
thought. John was on the point of making a disclaimer like "Good
heavens I'm not interested in the Odhams girl . . ." when he
stopped himself. It was as though someone had played a high
note on the organ in his father's church just before the blessing.

Charlie got up.

"She's twenty-five and she's mad about you."

He walked straight out of the room and John saw him

hurrying down the footpath towards the beach. It was raining and he hadn't got a coat.

Normally John would have gone after Charlie and questioned him relentlessly. What did he mean—mad? Was Miss Odhams mad? Was he saying she was keen on him—had she said so to him? If she had, why hadn't she told him—they'd often discussed her, and he'd never even hinted at such a thing—quite the opposite. But Charlie had seemed as though he didn't want to be followed. It was raining—really pelting down . . .

He looked at the bleak seascape, suddenly darkened, the heavy clouds rolling out to sea, and the bungalow seemed suddenly no longer a refuge. It sheltered him from the rain, maybe, but that's all. It couldn't protect him from lightning when it struck. And as if to answer him, the clouds split and the bungalow roof seemed to lift off and bang down again like a tin box lid.

"Good God," he said out loud. "The woman's in love with me." That's why Charlie had talked about getting married in the first place—he was trying to get a reaction. That's why he'd suggested picnics with Muriel—no it was John who'd suggested them, but all the same . . . And that's why Charlie had suddenly blurted it out and rushed off into the storm. He'd known for ages and was jealous. Poor Charlie. He put on his trench coat and took his umbrella and a raincoat for Charlie, and went off down the path which led to the promenade. Poor Charlie.

Charlie saw him coming. He was sheltering behind a beach hut. He knew what John would say. "Charlie if she really loves me, she'll have to love you too." Love me, love my dog, is what Charlie thought ruefully. John never questioned that Charlie belonged to him and he to Charlie.

It stopped raining just as suddenly as it had started. John gave Charlie his raincoat and they walked towards the office. "Don't be jealous, Charlieboy. And don't worry about our friendship. I'm not mad about Muriel, and if I ever am, you'll be the first to know. Because our friendship means more to me than half a dozen Muriels."

Charlie said nothing. He could see what was going to happen and it was the very last thing he wanted, and the very last thing that John wanted. But there it was. He couldn't tell John, and John would never dream of such a thing for himself.

3

John was a firm believer in mind over matter. By applying his intellect to a problem it could be solved. If, as occasionally happened, a solution didn't appear like the conclusion of a geometric theorem—"therefore the angle ABC = 25 degrees"— he would refer the whole question to God, and a few hours of regular prayer could even make the problem go away altogether.

After supper the two friends usually took a stroll along the beach, but the rain came back for several days and it wasn't till Friday, three days after Charlie's revelation, that they sat on the beach and watched the sun go down.

"I've been on the look out for the last three days," said John, "and I think you may well be right about Muriel. She's so shy it's difficult to tell, but I caught her looking at me sideways in the wing mirror. I asked her to come for a walk with me alone tomorrow evening, and she didn't refuse."

"I shall be going home anyway," Charlie said.

"I know. That's why I asked her. But I deliberately said 'alone' to see if she was put off."

The sea churned up against the pebbles, dragging them back and forth with eternal rhythm. Charlie threw a stone towards a boulder and watched it bounce into the waves.

"I've worked out a possible programme," said John. "I'd like your opinion."

Charlie hurled another pebble, almost viciously.

"Assuming Muriel's in love with me, I must be very careful how I approach her in future. I don't want to raise her hopes until I'm sure of my own feelings. Apart from anything else, Thompson has a prior claim on her. They're almost engaged."

"I've never heard him say he loves her," said Charlie.

"No, nor I. Nevertheless, he might be about to fall in love." He got out his diary and thumbed through the pages. "Another thing against getting too friendly is that if the Serbian job comes off, I could be away for a year. The War Office said they'd offer you a job as my assistant of course."

Charlie nodded. He was only half listening. How could anyone work out a programme for falling in love? Anyone except John of course. He took off his shoes and went down to the water's edge. The sea was quite warm. John joined him.

"Warm enough for a swim?" he asked.

"Will be when I get back."

"I wonder if Muriel likes swimming."

"Sure to."

They retraced their steps to the promenade. John thought Charlie was worrying about going home and being confronted by the usual arguments.

"Tell your mother that I've met a girl, and who knows what might happen! That'll please her."

"Sure to," said Charlie.

There was a red glow in the sky. "Red at night, shepherd's delight," said John. He put his arm round Charlie's shoulders. "I'm quite looking forward to going for a walk with Miss Odhams—Muriel. Her father's a partner in Odhams, by the way—I found that out—publishes *Tit Bits* and *The Daily Herald*. Did you know that?" Charlie sent a pebble ricocheting along the promenade.

"But I want her to understand right from the start that we are inseparable."

"She can't marry both of us," said Charlie.

"No, but she can *love* both of us, can't she?" He went on, "I'll tell you one thing, Charlie, I think Muriel's the nicest girl I've met—awfully nice—and jolly."

"I agree with you. She's stunning."

"You really think that?" John was excited.

"Yes I do—stunning."

"You wait till I tell her that."

Charlie tried to remonstrate with him. But John was more

determined than ever that Muriel should somehow be shared by both of them. He talked of nothing else all evening. He would write down everything that took place during the coming week, and Charlie could read it when he got back.

"It'll all be in my diary. I'll tell you everything as it happens."

Charlie frowned gloomily. "I'm going to bed. I've got to get off early."

It was only an excuse. How could he possibly tell John that he was already in love with Muriel himself?

John courted Muriel with Edwardian zeal and Victorian restraint. It was as though the war had never been, and he was still a Scots lad of eighteen, walking his young lady round the monument on a Sunday afternoon. The carefree 1920s were only a year away, but for John and Muriel they weren't even a dot on the horizon.

There were no agonising silences, fumblings and blushes. Muriel felt almost instantly relaxed. There would be no attempt to break down her reserves of shyness and force her to reveal her feelings. When John went for a walk, he walked for miles, and at a good four miles an hour. When he stopped, he stopped—sat down and talked—mostly about himself, but always with interest. He was insatiably curious, and if some detail cropped up with which he wasn't familiar, he'd look it up when he got home and next day tell Muriel as she drove him on official business. "By the way, Miss Odhams, the distance to Australia is nine thousand, three hundred and forty five miles . . . and a half, as the crow flies."

It wasn't till their third walk that he allowed himself to take her hand and noted in his diary that she had a firm grasp. But the walks became almost daily, and by the time Charlie returned, he was able to read in John's diary that Muriel had put her arms round John's neck, looked right into his eyes and called him "Darling". And that John had known she wanted him to kiss her on the lips, but he'd only kissed her hair.

"Why didn't you?" asked Charlie.

"Why didn't I what?" John knew perfectly well.

"Kiss her, of course? It was the same with that Christine girl—

she wanted you to kiss her and you didn't."

"I don't want to give Muriel the wrong idea."

"But good heavens," said Charlie impatiently, "you've been holding hands and cuddling for a fortnight . . !"

"Ten days."

"What's wrong about the idea of kissing her?"

John couldn't explain that if he kissed her he'd feel that he had to marry her, or at least get engaged. He said lamely:

"Her fiancé was killed during the war."

"All the more reason to kiss her."

Charlie was back to his usual cheery form, John noted. Obviously he'd got over his jealousy.

"Tell you what—why don't you come on our next walk? Maybe you'll give me some Dutch courage."

"I'm not going to sit beside you and nudge you when I think the moment's ripe."

"No, but she was asking when you were getting back, and said she hoped you'd come for a walk too. I told her that it felt funny going on a walk without you, Charlie. You see in the diary for Wednesday." He turned the page back: "I told Muriel I missed Charlie no end and that our friendship was the most important thing in life for me."

"All right, I'll come with you both," said Charlie.

"All three of us," said John.

"All three of us," said Muriel.

She was in the middle, and they linked hands and walked along the beach. John grasped her hand like a suitcase, but Charlie's hand was moist and trembling. Muriel didn't look at either of them. She was thinking of the day Charlie had said he loved her and asked her what she thought he ought to do about it. And she'd said: "I'm much too old for you"—three years!— and he'd asked her if Major Reith was too old for her, and she'd said, "No", very quickly. Anyway, Charlie seemed to have got over his calf love—that's what her mother called it—except for his trembling hand. So she walked happily on the beach away from Shoreham and the office and into the country.

They sat down and rested. Muriel gladly kicked off her shoes and waggled her toes.

"How far have we come?"

"Five miles," said John.

"I suppose in Scotland five miles is nothing."

"It's nothing in England—in Scotland it'd seem like ten."

"Up hill all the way," said Charlie.

"Remember that day we climbed the Cairngorms and got lost," said John.

"We must have gone twenty five miles."

"Nearer thirty!"

The two friends laughed. Muriel joined in. She felt that she was being let into a secret. The two friends wanted her to be a part of their past as well as the present.

"How did you both first meet?" she asked.

"1913," said Charlie. "But we weren't exactly strangers. Everybody in Glasgow knew John's father. And most people knew John the Giant. When I told my father I wanted to be friends with him, my father said, "Certainly you can be friends—so long as I don't have to sit behind him in church.""

"We used to take Communion together," John explained. "We discovered Jesus Christ together. What does he mean to you, Muriel?"

"Jesus Christ?" She smiled in surprise, then realised she was being asked a serious question. "Very little I'm afraid."

"Well that's honest," said John. "And hopefully, easily remedied."

Muriel wasn't sure how. Her family were not churchgoers, and she much preferred sitting in a garden to sitting in church.

"Shall we say a prayer together, Charlie?"

"All right."

"You start, Muriel,' said John.

"I don't know any prayers."

"You know the Lord's Prayer. That'll do."

"I'd rather not, thank you. I only pray in church."

"Is that a fact? Then next Sunday we'll go to church. Agreed?"

"Yes if you'll come to lunch with Mummy and Daddy," said Muriel.

Charlie was doubtful. "They won't want both of us."

"Of course they will. I shall tell them you're inseparable."
She gave them a hug.

"We're inseparable," she heard herself saying, and she joined the dream world that John had created for himself and Charlie.

4

July—the sun rose early, and so did John. He liked getting up anyway, and shaving and having a cold bath. It was easy for him to obey the latest dying instruction from his father: "Always get up at seven, my dear boy."

Charlie didn't mind so long as he was left undisturbed, but John had recently taken to singing loudly and cheerily. *"Cobble all day and cobble all night"* and *"We are the robbers of the woods"* . . . Chu Chin Chow followed by a pot-pourri of hymns and psalms. Charlie showed his irritation by banging on the cardboard wall behind the bed. John came in half-dressed.

"Oh you're awake," said John. "You were asleep when I got back. Do you know what happened when I took Muriel for a midnight walk?"

"No."

John sat down on the bed.

"She put her arms round my neck and looked into my eyes for a long time. And I said to her, 'Why are you looking into my eyes?'. She didn't say anything, so I asked her again and she said 'Kiss me', and I did. On the lips—several times. We must have been there for fifteen minutes or more."

Charlie lay back on his pillow and turned his head away.

"I'm in love with her, Charlie, no doubt about that. I didn't tell her of course," he added quickly. "But she's in love with me, and I'll tell her the next time. What do you think of that, Charlieboy?"

Charlie made no response, and John was much too full of his newfound happiness to notice the strain in the voice. "When are you going to ask her to marry you?"

"Oh, I haven't made up my mind about that," said John. "I've made some tea—do you want a cup?"

The next few days were purgatory for Charlie. Every evening
John would come back and relate some new detail of his
courtship. How Muriel had kissed his hand, how she'd put her
hand on his heart and vice versa—how she'd let her hair down
and it had blown in the wind—how beautiful she was and how
thoughtful and kind and gentle and sweet. How he wanted to
kiss her, how he did kiss her . . . It was too much for Charlie, and
one night when they were sitting by the fire reading peacefully
he made a sort of choking sound.

John looked across at him and saw that there were tears
rolling down his cheeks . . .

"Charlie, old boy . . ."

"I'm sorry, I'm sorry, but I can't help it, Johnnie. I'm so in love
with Musie, so in love with her. I always have been, I always will
be . . . I'm so sorry."

John went over to him and put his hands on his shoulders.

"What's there to be sorry about? Now that I know you love
her too I'm absolutely certain that I'm doing the right thing."

"What's that mean?"

"It means that I'm going to marry her. I've always told her that
we're inseparable, Charlie." He comforted him. "She understands and says she loves you. Now that I know you love her as
well, everything's going to be all right."

The words flowed over Charlie unheeded. All he seemed to
hear was John's voice repeating "Love" like some charm—a spell
that would drive away the evil spirits which seemed to surround
him. He went on sobbing, but eventually he took the clean
handkerchief John had thoughtfully fetched from a drawer, blew
his nose several times and recovered.

"I'm all right now," he said.

"Of course you are."

The next day John asked Muriel to stop the car before they went
to pick Charlie up from the depot. He explained poor Charlie's
situation and finished up by taking both her hands in his and
saying, "What it amounts to in a nutshell is that you've got two
men in love with you instead of one, so you should be twice as

happy."

"Will that spoil your friendship?" she asked anxiously.

"I've thought a lot about that. As long as you love us both, how can it?"

It was on the tip of her tongue to say, like Charlie, that she couldn't marry both of them. She remembered just in time that John hadn't even mentioned the subject. So she just nodded and smiled and gave him a kiss. "Perhaps I should talk to Charlie alone some time?" she said.

"That's a very good idea," said John enthusiastically. "Let's go and pick him up now and go for a walk."

An hour later, all three of them drove out into the country. Muriel stopped the car and got out. So did Charlie. John remained in his seat.

"Come on John," called Charlie from the top of a gate.

"You go on—I'll catch you up."

"He wants us to have a talk together Charlie," said Muriel.

"Alone?"

"Yes."

John watched them go off together. He saw them take hands, and then they were gone. He lit a cigarette. He'd give them ten minutes.

They were back in five, running to get him. The two people he held dearest in the world, running down the hillside, the sun behind them, running and calling. He let them open the car door and drag him out.

"Come up to the top of the hill," said Charlie, "the view's terrific."

They couldn't enjoy it without sharing it with me, thought John.

He strode along, easily getting to the top before them. It was a wonderful view—the line of the shore white and blue, a haze hanging over a shimmering sea. He breathed in the air like pure oxygen. He was King, and this was Camelot.

Charlie and Muriel came panting up beside him and Muriel took his hand.

"The view's not bad at all," said John. "Not as good as the top of the Cairngorms, mind, but not bad."

Muriel laughed and then suddenly turned and kissed Charlie.

Mrs Odhams found it very peculiar that her daughter should be habitually accompanied by two men, and bestow her favours equally. She found it even odder that neither of the men seemed to mind.

"But I'm not engaged to either of them, Mummy," she tried to explain.

Mrs Odhams had observed them throughout lunch and tea and almost till supper time, when John had leapt up and said, "Great Heavens, we must be going. Evensong is at 6.30."

She thought John a very serious young man, and when he turned the wounded side of his face towards her, well . . .

"Ghoulish." Her husband supplied the word.

"Oh, Daddy, he was wounded—he can't help it. I always look on the other side—the bright side."

"But even so . . ."

She stopped. After all there was no harm in Muriel having more than one boyfriend. And at least it showed that she'd finally got over Raymond. They'd only been engaged a month or so when the news came. Muriel had taken it very well, but the photograph was still on her dressing table.

"I think they're both very nice. But sooner or later you'll have to make the choice."

"I've made it already, Mummy, but he hasn't asked me."

"What do you think?" Mrs Odhams turned to her husband.

"He's very tall," he said.

John went up to London and walked round Hatton Garden, where he finally bought a diamond and pearl ring. He came back to Brighton the same day, and that evening, as Muriel and he sat in front of the fire, he brought it out and held it up so that the flickering firelight made it sparkle.

Muriel was thrilled. "What is it, John?" she asked, knowing perfectly well.

"It's a ring. I bought it today in Hatton Garden." And he put it back in his pocket.

Muriel stared at him. He looked so weird in the firelight, and he behaved so strangely. Why did he buy a ring for her and show it to her, and then not give it to her?

"What's wrong?" he asked.

"I'm frightened, John."

"Are you, Musie?" He leant over to her and took her hand. "Shall we say a wee prayer?"

The next day he went up to Scotland. Before he proposed to Muriel, he must at least tell his mother and father. He could have written, but he wanted to know what they really felt. He went in to see his father first, and sat with him. Then he got the ring out and let him look at it. The old man looked at it closely and handed it back.

"Very nice, and who's the lucky girl?"

John told him, but he seemed to lose interest very soon and didn't speak again. John left him when the night nurse arrived.

He had to wait to break the news to his mother. Jean seemed to be hanging round all the time. John, much to her annoyance, refused to be drawn into an argument and finally she went off to see the Hendersons. Then he told his mother, very tenderly, that he'd met the most wonderful girl whom he truly loved and who loved him, and that he wanted to marry her. That it'd make no difference to their relationship, because Muriel would love her too and she'd love Muriel . . .

His mother didn't want to look at the ring, and began to cry. "I've lost my boy, I've lost my boy. What will become of me?"

John wished he'd stopped at Brighton. He went straight down to Glasgow Central and booked a sleeper for the following night.

If his mother and father had been given a vote on Muriel, it'd have been one for, and one against, so he still didn't know if he ought to propose. He decided to give Charlie the casting vote.

Charlie was waiting for him at the station. Muriel was with her parents at Southwick. He hadn't told her he was coming back so soon, and he felt relieved to be alone with Charlie. The stresses and strains of the whole business were really getting him down. The joys of bachelordom were very sweet at that moment.

They went off for a meal, and were soon laughing and talking as though nothing had happened. He said as much to Charlie.

"Nothing *has* happened yet," said his friend. "I've never

known anyone take so long to pop the question. Mrs Odhams thinks you're mucking about with Muriel."

"Mucking about?"

"Well damnit all, you say you're in love with her, and she's in love with you, and you've shown her the ring and you still haven't popped the question."

"You think I should?"

"Of course you should. What more do you want? A sign from God?"

"I'd appreciate that very much, and pray every night."

Charlie laughed, and John looked disapprovingly at him and then laughed too. Charlie was the only person who could make him laugh whenever he wanted, could cheer him up and dust him down and leave him fresh and smiling. Dear Charlie.

"I'm still worried that it may spoil our friendship, Charlie. That's all it is. Tell me honestly—do you think it will?"

"Honestly I don't think it will."

"Because if you do, then the whole thing's off." John looked so earnestly at Charlie.

Charlie simply said, "Tomorrow we'll all three go for a walk, and you'll propose to Muriel."

"That's an order?"

"A prophesy."

John smiled in spite of himself. Dear Charlie—I'll miss him terribly if . . . But it didn't bear thinking about. The one thing that didn't occur to either of them was that Muriel might say "No".

5

The visiting General would not be rushed. He hadn't come all the way down from the Ministry of Munitions in order to be fobbed off with a quick tour round the perimeter of the depot. John humoured him by consulting him on the efficiency of the various types of grenades. The General handled them lovingly and reminisced about the retreat from Mons which had earned him rapid promotion as his H.Q. had been blown up by just such a box of grenades carelessly left around.

"I lost my little finger," he said. "How did you get yours?"

"Damned stupidity."

"Did you have any dealings with the Mills bomb?"

"Only with the results, sir. I was in the Engineers and before that in Transport."

"Transport?" said the General as though recalling the name of some distant relative. He examined the books without the faintest knowledge of what to look for—like someone with an hour to kill, browsing in a bookshop.

John showed no signs of impatience, but excused himself for a moment. He crossed the passage to Charlie's office and entered without knocking.

"Charlie, I can't get away for another hour at least. Will you nip back to the bungalow and fetch the ring? It's in a pair of socks in the left-hand top drawer. Tell Muriel she's to pick us up at five."

"Yes, sir," said Charlie, giving a mock salute.

John encountered the mess orderly. "Bring some tea for the General, Cooper. In a large enamel mug with lots of sugar."

"Yes, sir."

The General stopped browsing when tea was duly served as John had prescribed. "A bit of the real McCoy" he said, sipping appreciatively. "Takes you back, eh Reith?"

He left fifteen minutes later, pausing to tap the lintel over the door. "Mind you don't catch your head on this. We used to have an old rubber tube over the dug-out door. Saved a lot of nasty bruises."

"But not fingers, sir."

The General laughed and left, pleased with himself and with Major Reith.

John tidied his desk. When he came in to work the next day, there'd be no clutter to greet him. He'd been taught by the nursemaid he detested to finish every scrap on the plate before asking for a second helping.

Colonel Thompson entered.

"Well, that went off all right. The General was delighted."

"Yes. We compared our wounds. By the way, are you still interested in Muriel Odhams?"

"What, as a driver? Oh . . ." he realised. "No, no, you carry on, John. Count me out. I'm not good enough for her. In any case she's in love with someone else. God bless you."

He gave a saintly smile and left on tiptoe so as not to disturb the beauty of the moment.

"What a prig the man is," thought John and went off to join Charlie and Muriel who were waiting for him in the Sunbeam.

"Beachy Head, Miss Odhams," said John as they drove off. "Did you find what you were looking for, Charlie?"

"The socks? Yes," said Charlie, and tapped his waistcoat pocket.

They drove through to Eastbourne in silence, and the car took the steep road to the top of the headland with scarcely a groan. Muriel was an excellent driver as well as everything else.

"Put it off the road, under the tree," John ordered. "We'll walk along the top."

He was familiar with the path, and had decided on the exact spot for the proposal. He wanted somewhere memorable and high up. Muriel was aware that something was going on, but didn't try to jolly things along. She took her cue from the two men who walked on either side of her, holding her hands in wordless communion.

Then Charlie said: "I'm tired. I'm going to sit down. You two go on together." He pressed the diamond ring into John's hand.

"All right, Charlie. You stay here. Musie and I will only be just over the brow there."

Charlie watched them walking hand in hand along the cliff top. They stopped but after a moment Charlie saw Muriel go on, while his friend hurried back to join him.

"What's up John? Did she say no?"

"I haven't asked her yet. Charlie, are you quite certain that I should ask her?"

"You've got to decide that for yourself."

"But are you sure you wouldn't rather marry her? You love her."

"So do you, Johnnie, and she loves you."

"You think so?"

"I know so. You love her, she loves you . . . and she doesn't love me. Now go and ask her—for your own sake, and for my sake."

He turned his friend round like a dummy and gave him a little push towards Muriel who stood waiting patiently on the brow. She'd taken her large summer hat off and was shading her eyes in the sunlight, watching a sailing boat bobbing about far below. She turned as John approached. He'd prepared what he was going to say—indeed rehearsed it for Charlie's benefit. He stopped and took off his hat. His mouth was suddenly dry, and he heard himself saying the words. He was like an actor making his first appearance as Richard III—opening the play with a huge speech and the whole drama ahead of him. He knew the lines perfectly, but how would the audience react?

"Muriel, I'm not much, but I try to be better. If you put your life in mine, and trust me, I shall do all I can to make you happy. Do you love me enough to take this step?"

Muriel went to him and kissed him and said, "Yes, John."

She was so simple and direct. John was so complex. He stood with her only a second or two, then he turned to look for his friend. Charlie was standing with his back to them, and John whistled him up to join them. Charlie must have heard, but he gave no sign. In a moment John had left Muriel and run back to his friend. He put his arms round him. He felt bereft that Charlie had somehow gone. Charlie could only think of Muriel, and there were no tears in his eyes. He walked past his friend and took Muriel in his arms and said, "Mu, Darling, I'm so pleased."

He took her hands in his, her fingers enclosed his.

"But where's the ring? John, you haven't given her the ring!"

"I knew there was something missing."

John took the ring from his pocket and put it on Muriel's finger. It fitted perfectly and they all admired it. Suddenly John kissed it, and then held her wrist and showed it to Charlie, and Charlie kissed it too. Muriel took her hand away and put the ring to her own lips. For her it was a spontaneous act of love, but for John it was all part of a private ritual which he had devised, and which only he understood. The public ritual of being engaged to a girl who would one day become his wife was something he couldn't understand at all. Nor did he wish to.

Muriel, John and Charlie were all in love, and for a few weeks able to inhabit John's dream world undisturbed. It was enough for Mr and Mrs Odhams to have their daughter safely engaged, and John's parents were three hundred miles away. The sun shone at Brighton, and the three friends joined the thousands of others who were determined to "get back to normal as soon as possible", and forget the dank and dismal trenches. They spent hours on the beach, and John read Tennyson and Wordsworth:

Bliss was it in that dawn to be alive

But to be young was very heaven!

Then came the telegram—and for a second it seemed that the war had returned. John handed it to Muriel. "Father's had a stroke. I'll catch the next train." He packed a heavy leather suitcase and Muriel put some sweetpeas in the top. He wore his uniform. He kissed her goodbye at the station as he leant out of the window. She was holding Charlie's hand.

The overnight from Euston was crowded, and hardly a uniform in sight. The war was over and he realised with a shock that he'd soon be demobbed himself. His job was done, the factories reverting to peaceful products, the flow of munitions down to a trickle. He must ring up Osborne at the Ministry and ask him if there was any news of the Serbian job. And he'd remind him of his promise to put Charlie's name forward for an O.B.E.. It wasn't much, but an O.B.E. at 23 was not bad. And it might serve to remind Mrs Bowser that her son's great friend wasn't too bad either!

He fell asleep and dreamed that he was back in the old nursery at the top of the Manse. He was all alone, and then Muriel came in and put her arms round him and kissed him.

His father was unable to speak. He could move his hands though, and John spent almost the whole of his first day at home sitting with him. He read from the Family Bible, and prayed for all the family in turn. Beth had been and gone before he'd arrived—he was sorry to miss her—Archie was there with his things all over John's bedroom, and Robert, whose first words to him were, "Have you brought your cheque book? I want to borrow a hundred pounds!"

What a cad Robert was. And Jean was there too—nagging away at her mother even when she was in her father's room. John told the old man that when he died he wouldn't look after Jean on account of the way she'd treated him and mother. His father agreed—nodding his head and moving his hand. The next day John sat on one side of the bed, while his mother sat on the other. They didn't say anything, simply held a hand each and prayed silently. Miraculously their prayers were answered—Mr Reith's speech returned slowly and painfully. John recorded the words in his diary fearing they might be the last.

"Make your peace with God, John and think much of Jesus Christ."

John thought about Muriel and Charlie. He couldn't leave Father, and he wanted them both up there with him. He wrote a long letter to Charlie and a short one to Muriel. A few days later he got their replies in the same envelope. Muriel said she'd asked Charlie to come and stay at Southwick, and that her mother had taken her on one side and said she was completely mystified by "what was going on". And her brother Edward had been very tactless and said over dinner, "I can't make out who you're going to marry—John or Charles." Charles had left early, and it was "All simply dreadful".

John understood—he'd experienced the same sort of treatment when he'd been there one weekend. Muriel and he had been for a walk and come in and gone straight up to his bedroom for a chat. And they hadn't been there five minutes when Mrs Odhams called up the stairs: "Are you coming Muriel?" He felt really angry, and would have gone that minute if it hadn't been for Muriel, who'd made blackcurrant tea specially. Mrs Odhams called again: "I can't think what you two find to talk about."

Charlie said there was nothing left to do at the office and he was thinking of coming home and would bring Muriel. John looked up a train and wired back: "Will meet the 5.10 from Euston Thursday." It was high time Muriel was introduced to mother and father. High time that she and her family were made aware that he was not going to be pushed into marriage. The wedding would take place when he decided, and on his terms, when he was ready.

6

Muriel was no stranger to Scotland. Part of Odhams Press was installed there, and she'd spent every summer holiday since she was five in the Highlands. She knew and liked the Scots, otherwise she'd never have fallen for John. Her father—also a "John"—was content to leave business decisions to Uncle William, and domestic ones to his wife. Her sister Doris was devoted to her, and her brother Edward the same. They had no very firm opinions about anything, except for the German bomb which had destroyed one of Odhams' Printing works. Muriel, like her cousins and uncles and aunts, had shares in the family business. She was proud of Odhams and her family, which was a happy one. It came as a considerable shock when she found herself thrown into the midst of an abrasive, discontented and unloving Scots family, still dominated by a dying Presbyterian clergyman who was held in as much awe and esteem as the Archbishop of Canterbury.

She wanted to run back home, but she was deeply in love, and the prickly Reiths were totally disarmed by her innocent good nature. They'd somehow always expected John to bring home a sharp and clever lady from Edinburgh. Mrs Reith, who was English herself, remembering her own first years in Scotland, did all she could to ease her future daughter-in-law into the whalebone corset of the kirk. But whereas she'd always been a firm believer in Christianity, Muriel was only a very pallid member of the Church of England. This was a disadvantage in some respects, but, as John pointed out at least she was "Virgin territory" and he made it his business to inform her mind. Muriel didn't much like readings from the Bible and prayers, but she took up knitting and tried not to click her needles too loudly. Eventually even John understood that Muriel so willing to oblige in other respects, was never going to be a great one for prayer and meditation. She, like her fiancé, had her own terms for getting married.

A month later John was demobilised at the Crystal Palace. He met Muriel in London Wall by Cleopatra's Needle. John always attached great importance to meeting places. Cleopatra's Needle had the aura of two thousand years. Muriel was more interested in the German U-Boat *Deutschland* which was moored opposite.

"Well," said John, "I'm now out of work for the first time in my life."

"What about Serbia?"

"No good. Osborne's like Egypt, a broken reed. but he's got Charlie his O.B.E."

"Oh, that's marvellous."

"Coming from Osborne—yes. There's Mr Niven, of course."

"Mr Niven?"

"Friend of my father. I could join him as his assistant. It'd be two thousand a year, but it'd mean going to Bombay."

"I wouldn't mind that."

"You're not going to Bombay, Musie."

"But . . ."

"You've seen what happened to Jean. She's bringing her divorce case, did you hear that? No consideration for anybody!"

They went to see *Tilly of Bloomsbury*. They enjoyed it, but John felt guilty that he was not at home. His father was going downhill rapidly. His mind wandered dreadfully and he wanted people he knew round him.

They went down to Southwick and Mrs Odhams was reasonably polite—Muriel had told her that John was worrying about his father, so she didn't come out with her usual question, "When's the wedding?" He had a word with Mr Odhams though, and said he couldn't think of getting married till he had a job or at least a very good prospect. Mr Odhams sympathised, and asked rather pointedly after "Young Bowser". John told him he'd got the O.B.E. which shut him up. But he sensed the growing antagonism within the Odhams' household and was glad to get back to Scotland.

The weather had turned very cold. Glasgow was colder than at
any time since 1869. He managed to find a tram that was
running, but he had to walk most of the way from the station. He
went straight to see his father and sat with him. He was worse,
the eyes sunken hollows. He kept saying, "Make your peaces
with God." John wasn't sure if he was talking to him or to
himself. He could hear Jean screaming at her mother. He wanted
to stay with his father, to be with him at the end, but Charlie had
gone to London and Glasgow seemed bare and empty without
him.

"Get up at seven," murmured his father.

Mr Bowser had suggested his name to Sir William Beardmore
for General Manager. But he couldn't apply for the job unless he
was asked.

"Take Jesus Christ into your counsels, John."

He'd go back to London, stay at the Regents Palace. If father
got worse, mother would telephone him there.

"Be at peace. Goodbye dear boy."

He went back to London and saw *Cyrano de Bergerac* with
Charlie and Muriel. He loved them both as much as ever. He
told Charlie he'd try to get a job at Beardmore's and then he'd
get him appointed as his second-in-command. And he told
Muriel that once he'd got the job, they'd find a house near
Glasgow and get married. Muriel said she'd like to get the
furniture from Whiteley's so they went for a walk round the
store. They were happy as ever—all three of them. And Charlie
had his O.B.E.

That night John dreamed that he gathered his father up in his
arms and carried him to the study and laid him on the couch.
And the next night he dreamed again that he was at home. It was
Sunday morning, the church bell was ringing, and his father
leant on his arm and they walked to church together.

He was having breakfast when the telegram came: Father
passed away peacefully this morning at three.

John buried his father. He kept the coffin lid open till the last
moment, so that he could look at the dear face. He put a sprig of

white lilac in his father's hands and closed the lid.

He put every detail down in his diary. He would never forget the day on which his father died, and never cease to reproach himself for not being at the bedside.

"Goodbye dear boy."

7

Sir William Beardmore's office door remained closed. John eyed it with growing impatience. He'd come to the Coatbridge Factory expecting to be ushered in deferentially and immediately offered the post of General Manager, plus bonus. He'd made up his mind about the bonus. If he was to rescue the firm he'd require a share in the profits. And with his experience both in America and at Shoreham, he had no doubt that he could revive the flagging Beardmore rotary pumps and oil engines, and get the Beardmore cars and taxis back on the road. But an hour had passed, and still he was waiting. His early enthusiasm began to fade.

He looked at the brown panelled walls and smoky windows. He thought it extraordinary that a man should spend half his life in a dingy room in order to spend the other half asleep in a vast mansion. When he became Chairman of Beardmore's his office would be his study, with decent wallpaper and flowers and pictures, and a decent view from the window. Not a cramped collection of tin roofs. He wasn't sure now that he even wanted the job any more. In his heart he knew he was applying for it for the worst reason in the world. "Better love Jesus than be a millionaire, and better a millionaire than a politician" was one of his father's dictums. But the reason he wanted the money was because now that his father was dead, although John was the youngest of the family, he seemed to be the only one capable of earning any money. The Manse was being sold. He'd have to find a house for his mother and Jean, and one for himself. He couldn't marry Muriel unless he had an income and a house.

Another fifteen minutes passed. He might as well go. He'd

much rather live in London. He'd get a job there at some Ministry or other. He wasn't going to spend his life in Glasgow in a car factory!

He got up.

"Sorry to keep you waiting, Mr Reith. Been on holiday—only just got back!" Sir William clasped his hand warmly and drew him into his office.

Half an hour later John re-emerged as the future General Manager of Beardmore's with a salary of £1,200 a year—plus bonus! Sir William drove off in his Rolls, and John took a taxi home, which he noted was not a Beardmore. He'd start his new job in three weeks. Meanwhile he'd clear out the Manse and then take a holiday.

He bounded up the stairs. His mother's bedroom was locked. He could hear Jean going on at her, and her mother crying. He banged on the door and Jean came out.

"What's going on Jean?"

"She's having one of her bouts. I said she should cheer up and stop feeling sorry for herself."

John went in to see his mother, and Jean called after him, "Be gentle with her." He could have hit her. Be gentle—how dare she say that to him, as though he were ever anything else where Mother was concerned?

"Mother, I've got the job as General Manager of Beardmore's, so I'm going to find you a new house."

This news set his mother off again and he went out into the garden and lit a large bonfire to burn the rubbish. The sooner they left the Manse the better. He didn't want to remember it as a place of continual quarrelling. He used to play in the garden like any other child, kick a ball about, let off fireworks, light bonfires . . . And now he was burning the rubbish of ages and his childhood home was being sold to a Catholic panel doctor!

He suddenly remembered it was Muriel's birthday next week, so went off and bought her a suitcase—and one for his mother whose seventieth birthday was due the following month. His spirits had risen again, and he decided to go up to London as soon as possible. He sat with his mother after supper and played the harmonium. Then he realised she was sobbing quietly. He stopped and put his arms round her to comfort her. She wept bitterly, then smiled and gave him a kiss and said she felt much better. John wished that Douglas and Beth and Archie and even Robert would occasionally lend a hand. He was glad he was still her "wee bairn" but he was also about to get married and from today was General Manager of Beardmore's.

He rang up Muriel at the "Homestead" and gave her the good news. She said she was thrilled, but was a bit subdued and that her mother would like a word with him. Mrs Odhams came on the line, sounding very cold and distant. She said she hoped he'd be coming down soon as she wished to discuss Muriel's trousseau.

"Her trousseau? I don't know anything about such things. She can wear what she likes."

"Nevertheless, John, I should still like to see you. And so would Muriel. It's nearly a year since you became engaged."

So that was it.

"I shall be in London this week on business, so I'll come down and see you."

Mrs Odhams handed the phone back to Muriel. Muriel sounded relieved and asked John to be sure to let her know the train so that she could meet him. "Promise?" she said.

"Promise."

She sounded so suspicious and yet he was full of love.

Muriel was there at the station to meet him, and he gave her the suitcase right away.

"I thought you'd forgotten, John."

"I never forget a birthday, Musie. You'll find that out. I shall give you fifty birthday presents before I die."

She kissed him and then explained the mystery of the trousseau.

"Charlie was down here last week."

"Yes, he told me."

"Anyway, we went to a dance, and Edward came back and said he'd been there too and that he'd seen us and that it was obvious that Charlie was in love with me."

"Well?"

"Well Mummy was very upset."

"You mean she doesn't know that he's in love with you?" John was amazed that Muriel had never mentioned it to her parents.

"No."

"Then you'd better tell her."

"No."

"Why not?"

"She wouldn't understand. Don't say anything, please, John. As long as she knows that we're in love, that's all that matters." John looked doubtful. "We are in love aren't we?"

"I am," he said. "I can't speak for you."

"Oh, I love you, John. More than anyone in the world."

She kissed him again and nearly drove the car into the ditch. John didn't mind at all. But he thought privately that Edward Odhams was a blinking nuisance, and that the next time he came to visit his future in-laws he'd come down in the Coatbridge Austro-Daimler, and take Muriel back with him for a short tour of the Highlands.

He suggested this over dinner. Mrs Odhams said she was delighted, and her mind now quite at rest. But Mr Odhams asked him whether Charlie would be going with them, and seemed to be making innuendos which John didn't like.

"As a matter of fact, Charlie's going to be my assistant at Coatbridge, so I shall leave him in charge while I'm away."

"Will he be your best man at the wedding—whenever that is?"

"Most certainly he will."

What was the man going on about?

"And the wedding will take place when we've had time to choose a house."

"Oh? So it could be next month?"

"Next year," said John without smiling.

Beardmore's had been featherbedded with government contracts during the war and was suffering the consequence. They'd lost their markets—one glance at the books was enough for John to see this. A tour of the factory revealed an ominous split between management and workers. The General Manager was looked upon with sullen resentment. John didn't take long to find the reason. The door of Sir William's office remained firmly closed to the workers. Not that it would have made much difference if it had been open all day long—he was rarely there, preferring the life of a country gentleman.

John set about his reforms with customary zest. His door was open to all-comers, and he was as much at home on the factory floor as any of his workers. He'd been through the mill and had trudged to work with his sandwiches and a flask of tea while the hooter blared—they couldn't tell him anything about the misery of engineering in Scotland in 1920. So he saw to it that improvements were made to the day-to-day conditions, that a bonus scheme was introduced and that "slackers" were weeded out.

This meant sackings and as it was either that or going out of business, he applied himself to the task with ruthless efficiency, selecting the men himself in some cases. His greatest stumbling block was a shop steward called Aitken, who had noticed the absence of leadership and discipline, and had determined to fill the gap. To him, Sir William was a parasite—he should be got rid of and the workers should take over. John heard him out several times—on the floor and in his office—though in the office he insisted on his removing his hat.

Sir William knew Aitken of old. He knew he was disruptive, but feared his power over his fellow workers. John had no such qualms. "The man's a Bolshevist, Sir William, he'll have to go."

"Aitken? Oh he's been with us right through the war."

"So have a good many other people, and they'll have to go as well." He mentioned members of the management. "They'll get their cards on the same day as Aitken gets his."

Sir William didn't protest. Young John Reith was so sure of himself, and someone had said the order books were picking up.

John summoned Aitken to his office, gave him a month's pay and sacked him. At five o'clock he went down to the main gate. The whistle went and he watched the men coming out. They assembled on the tarmac and Aitken addressed them. John noted that they listened attentively for fifteen minutes. So did John. The man wasn't rabble-rousing, he was saying goodbye. John was almost sorry for him. Almost.

Sir William was still in his office—unnaturally late leaving. John had given him a short list of members of the staff he intended getting rid of. The Chairman didn't like the idea at all. John entered briskly. "Aitken's gone," he announced. "Now if we lose White and Stephenson I can bring in an excellent assistant General Manager. You know him I expect. Mr Bowser's son Charles. He was my assistant at the Marine Engineering Depot. Just got the O.B.E."

Charlie had a flat in London, and was comfortably ensconced. John had stayed with him several times, and liked the area so much he'd tried to find a house nearby. He realised that it he were to fulfill his destiny he'd have to live in the capital eventually. There wasn't a house that he fancied, but he took out a half-yearly subscription to Charlie's local church in Regent Square. He didn't fancy the church either, but he liked the music and for Charlie's sake he wanted to belong to the congregation.

He rang Charlie the same evening and offered him the job of Assistant General Manager. Charlie didn't hesitate. If the call had come from Bombay or Serbia he'd have booked his passage immediately. It came from Scotland, and he arrived in Glasgow three days later. John had a room prepared at his flat, and the two friends were once more in harness together.

For over two months they worked flat out to save Beardmore's from extinction. Businesses were collapsing all round them. The patient hovered between life and death—life being in the hands of John and Charlie, and death being meted out by a Board which didn't know what to do, and didn't want to admit it, and so preferred to go on in the same old way. John, having prescribed the cure, would not alter it. Gradually the patient recovered, and though not completely out of danger, was well enough to allow the doctors to take a short holiday.

"Telephone Musie and tell her we'll come down to Southwick by car and bring her back with us."

John had decided to concentrate production on the car side of the business. He could learn to drive on the way to Brighton. He wasn't a complete beginner, having done a bit of motoring in America. But he hadn't actually sat at the wheel of a motor vehicle since 1917.

"We'll go in the Austro-Daimler, and do it in comfort."

Two days and several breakdowns later—not to mention four punctures—they reached Southwick. Mrs Odhams gave them her usual frosty reception, but they stayed the night and next morning John suggested that they all go up to London together. Mrs Odhams, as expected, declined the invitation. Muriel drove and in spite of four more punctures and wheezing halts every six miles, they didn't finally abandon the Austro-Daimler till Hammersmith.

It was all adventure, and laughter and fun—the three of them got on so well together, and Muriel looked more lovely than he'd ever seen her. "She'll look even more lovely once she's married," he confided to himself. He was about to repeat the thoughts out loud, when he stopped.

In the past he would have shared his thoughts with his friend—he might even have told Muriel, and they would have all three shared the same pleasure and excitement. But now he sensed the constraints which had grown up. He sensed the pain which lurked in Muriel's eyes as she strove to keep off the one subject which was uppermost in her mind and which provoked her mother to daily argument. He sensed a sadness in Charlie which had not been there before. It worried him, and spoiled the flavour of the occasion—as though someone had put sugar on his porridge.

By the time they arrived back in Glasgow, where he'd arranged for Muriel to stay with the Hendersons, he'd made two very important decisions. First, that in future a Beardmore would replace the Austro-Daimler as the company car, and, secondly, that it was time Charlie got married.

8

John might have been forgiven for thinking that to get a new car for the Company would be a lot easier than finding a wife for Charlie. Precisely the opposite. The Austro-Daimler suffered many more punctures, ran for weeks without a windscreen, and finally drove head first into a telegraph pole before a proud new 30-horsepower Beardmore was allocated to the General Manager. John always talked of the Austro-Daimler as though it had a life of its own. The fact that he was at the wheel when the accidents occurred was only coincidental. He was in no way to blame. Had it not skidded it would not have gone in the ditch—it took the corner too fast and hit the telegraph post etcetera, etcetera. The same attitude prevailed over his choice of a wife for Charlie. And, perhaps, like the Austro-Daimler, she was driven too fast.

From the moment that Charlie mentioned that he was even vaguely attracted to Maisie Henderson, John trod on the gas. The Hendersons were old family friends, and Maisie was an heiress. "She's got 1,500 acres of good land and a dowry of £20,000. I'm surprised you never thought of her before, Charlieboy."

"I'm surprised that you didn't, Johnnie."

"Och, she's not my type. But I daresay I could have led her to the altar if I'd had a mind to."

He made Maisie sound like some faded spinster, which she wasn't at all, being quite vivacious and spoiled and not at all the sort of girl to let John Reith boss her about. During Muriel's stay, she saw quite a lot of him and Charlie, and told Muriel she much preferred Charlie. Muriel passed the news on to John who passed it on to Charlie.

"It sounds to me like love at first sight, Charlieboy."

"Oh nonsense."

"The proof of the pudding . . .," replied John. "On Saturday we'll all go off in the Beardmore to see Douglas and Ada at Clunie." Ada got on well with Maisie and liked Charlie and would surely approve.

By the time Muriel returned to Southwick, Maisie and Charlie were going everywhere together, and John was rubbing his hands with glee and talking of marriage. But there was still no date fixed for his own wedding, and Robert said he thought Charlie'd be first past the post. He made various other disgusting comments and then had the nerve to spend an hour and a half trying to cadge another hundred pounds. John saw Muriel off on the train.

"John, don't you love me?"

"Of course I do."

"Then why can't we get married?"

"I told your mother we'd be married next year, and we will. And that's a fact."

"But it's all so vague," Muriel protested.

"Let's get done with Christmas, then we can name the date."

"Promise?"

"Promise."

He kissed her. The train pulled out. He hoped he'd said the right thing and hurried back to Charlie.

He couldn't give a date for his own wedding till he had a date for Charlie's. He found Charlie quite contentedly reading.

"Where did you get to? I thought you and Maisie were coming to see Muriel off."

"We went shopping. She had to buy some clothes to go skiing."

"Oh? Are you going with her?" John asked hopefully.

"No fear. She's going to Switzerland."

"Switzerland? When?"

"Next week. For a month."

"A month!"

He did a rapid calculation. That was all over Christmas and the New Year—just the time when he might have expected things to have got moving on the wedding front. He decided to drop the matter.

"What's that you're reading?"

"Book about China. Maisie gave it to me."

John took it from him and looked inside. "To dearest Charles with lots of love from Maisie. Happy Xmas."

"Very nice. What did you give her?"

"A sort of gold belt thing she seemed to fancy. Cost the earth."

"Maisie wouldn't think about that. She's got money to burn."

He returned the book.

"Why a book on China?"

"I might be going there. Import export for a friend of Father. It's very vague—probably never come off."

"You never know." He tried to be casual. Charlie wouldn't go, he knew that, but he could see Mrs Bowser's hand at work. She'd do anything to get him away from John. "What's Maisie say? Does she want you to go?"

"I don't think she minds one way or the other."

"Don't be daft man, she's in love with you. And in my opinion you're in love with her. Go on, admit it. I don't mind, in fact I'm delighted."

Charlie admitted it, and by admitting it gave John the opening he was looking for.

"Right," said John, "then the next thing we have to do is to find out definitely whether she's in love with you."

Charlie nodded. He wasn't sure how he'd got into this situation, he wasn't even sure what the situation was, but he knew that John had taken over, and that he had no need to worry about anything.

John threw himself into the role of marriage broker with his usual singlemindedness. He was totally incapable of half measures. He would play "Cyrano de Bergerac" to Maisie's "Roxana." He didn't think of himself as a Svengali. He took Charlie's hand in his. "Remember when you turned me round and gave me a little push towards Musie? Well, now it's my turn to do the same for you."

The memory of that occasion brought tears welling up in Charlie's eyes. He was still in love with Muriel.

"I can't help it Johnnie. There's hardly a day passes when I don't think of her and miss her."

John didn't allow his natural feelings of sympathy to interfere with the task in hand. He knew Charlie very well—he didn't like making decisions, which was why John was so good for him. Making decisions was meat and drink to John.

"Now, let's map out a plan of campaign. Now that we know you love Maisie . . ."

Charlie tried to protest.

John went on: "Now that you love Maisie, the next thing is to find out if she loves you. So what we'll do is this. We'll both see her off to Switzerland and see how she gets on with me . . ."

"If she doesn't there's no question of getting engaged," said Charlie fervently.

"I'll be on my best behaviour," said John. "Then, after she's been in Switzerland for a week, I'll write her a letter saying that I'm very worried about you. I'll say that you're in love with her, but you've been offered this job in China."

"Oh, I shan't go to China, never fear."

"I know you won't, but Maisie doesn't. And if she's in love with you, she'll write back by return begging me to try and stop you. That'll be proof certain that she loves you."

He waited for this to sink in.

"What happens then?" asked Charlie.

"I'll tell you that once we hear from Switzerland."

"Thank you, John. I feel so much better, I really do." Charlie was relieved and grateful.

They saw Maisie off at the station as planned. She was wrapped up in the most marvellous set of furs, with enough baggage to go to Siberia. She kissed John warmly and John responded without much enthusiasm. As he'd said to Charlie in the first place, Maisie wasn't his sort. He very much doubted if he was her sort either. But the smoke and noise and steam of Glasgow Central blanketed their feelings, and John reminded himself that it was Charlie she was after, not him. Even so, he knew that Maisie would never take both of them to her heart like Muriel. He hinted darkly that he would be writing to her in a day or two and left it at that. The whistle went, the guard waved his

green flag, and the engine thundered with elephantine excitement, its wheels skidding on the icy line. Crisp air and blue
skies awaited Maisie. For John and Charlie there was a week's
more slog at the factory before Christmas with Douglas at
Clunie.

The man on the main gate saluted smartly as John and Charlie
drove the newest Beardmore away from the factory. John at the
wheel allowed himself a sliver of satisfaction. It was a cheerful
salute, cheerfully returned by one of three hundred men who
recognised that Christmas might have been a miserable and
hungry one, but for the new General Manager and his Assistant.
John always made certain that Charlie was given full credit for
his work, just as he made certain that all workers got their fair
share of praise. Neither in public nor in private would he blow
his own trumpet. "Whatsoever things are of good repute" could
be relied upon to speak for themselves. Hence only a sliver of
satisfaction as he went to collect Jean and his mother from their
temporary accommodation.
     They piled the luggage and presents in the boot and Mother
and Jean into the back seat. Mother was a bit apprehensive on the
journey—there was thick snow, and more on the way. Jean
remarked that she hadn't expected to see Charlie.
     "Won't your mother be disappointed, Charlie? She told me
she was so looking forward to you spending Christmas at home."
     She knew just how to irritate her brother. Jean didn't let the
matter rest there either. She talked incessantly of Muriel and the
wedding—what did they want for a present?
     "I can't afford much, as you know, but weddings don't happen
very often."
     "Unlike divorces," shouted John over his shoulder, which shut
her up. It was bad enough trying to stay on the road, without
having Jean moaning about her poverty. The car was slithering
about all over the place, and finally got stuck halfway up a hill.
John reversed down to the bottom by a cottage. There was a
dustbin full of ash by the back door. Without disturbing the
occupants, he shoved it on the running board, and Charlie
shovelled out the ash as they crept back up the hill, arriving

exhausted but triumphant at Clunie.

Douglas and Ada made them very welcome at their Manse, and John was glad they'd come. Muriel had asked him to go down to Southwick, but he'd said he had to stay for his mother's sake. Which was perfectly true. Besides, he wanted to be on the spot when Maisie's letter came from Switzerland. He didn't mention that he wanted to see the New Year in with Charlie like he always did.

New Year's Eve meant a great deal more to John than downing a frugal glass of Scotch. It meant looking back over the old year, considering it in detail, drawing conclusions, assessing personal relationships and failures—never successes—and finally a decent burial. He understood death. He'd seen it often and come within inches of it himself. He was not afraid of it. He kissed the old year goodbye, just as he'd kissed his father's waxen forehead. He laid a sprig of lilac upon the clasped hands—a flower for the living—and as the clock struck twelve he closed the coffin lid.

The pains and sorrows and mistakes of 1920 were no more. The hopes and glories of 1921 yet to come. He raised his glass and linked arms with Charlie and the family, and sang *Auld Lang Syne* and recited Tennyson:

"Ring out the old, ring in the new . . ."

They went back to Glasgow the next day, leaving Mother and Jean behind, and dumping the empty dustbin.

Maisie's reply was on the doormat. John picked it up and read it without bothering to close the front door. He called to Charlie who was unloading the car.

"She loves you Charlie!"

"What?"

"She loves you! Maisie Henderson says she loves you!"

"Ring out the old, ring in the new . . . What a wonderful start to 1921!"

Charlie took the letter from him, dumping a suitcase. Maisie was obviously very distressed at the thought of him going to China. She asked if she should cut short her holiday in Switzerland.

"Cut short her holiday," exclaimed Charlie, amazed. "Good

heavens she must be jolly keen."

"I told you she was."

"What shall I do?"

"Nothing. There's a picture postcard for you." He handed it to him. "Send her one of the monument if you like. Don't mention her letter, you're not supposed to know anything about it."

"What are you going to do?"

"I'll write back in a day or two—keep her in suspense. I'll say you won't be making up your mind about China till she returns."

"Then what?" asked Charlie anxiously.

"Why then it's up to you, Charlieboy."

"Yes, yes, I suppose it is. But . . . but you will advise me?"

"Advise, yes—but not instruct. You must make up your own mind about a thing like this. Take your time. Maisie'll wait for you I'm sure."

Charlie was quite cockahoop for a time. They went to the Western Club and John drafted a reply to Switzerland and wrote a long letter to Muriel, telling her everything. He would have no secrets from Muriel . . . now or ever. So he wrote: "Charlie is over the moon already. Once I've got him engaged we can give you mother a date for our wedding. We might even have a double one."

Maisie returned at the end of the month and fell into Charlie's arms according to plan. John allowed the courtship to develop naturally, and Charlie spent a lot of time at "Argaty"—the Henderson country estate where life was very free and easy and far removed from the strait-laced atmosphere which Charlie encountered in other Scottish homes. Mrs Henderson made no secret of her liking for him and the Bowsers. He was one of the family.

John began to be suspicious that Charlie had not gone as far as he wanted. He enjoyed Maisie's company, but wasn't sure he wanted it for life. John could sympathise—he could hardly stand Maisie for ten minutes, let alone ten years. On the other hand she went out of her way to be nice to him. She cultivated Muriel's friendship, and whenever possible would give her a kiss and then give John one. She was a great one for kissing, and

John got very irritated one time when he had to stand waiting at the front door at "Argaty" while Maisie had a "Prolonged oscillatory performance" with her brother.

However she said time and again how fond she was of him, and that the last thing she wanted was to come between him and Charlie. "I know how much you mean to him, and that's why I'm so fond of you, John." (She'd called him "John" the first time she met him.)

Oddly enough, the more that Maisie had let her feelings come out in the open, the more reluctant Charlie became. He kept telling John that Maisie and he were as good as engaged, but John saw no signs of it. Charlie could not bring himself to actually ask Maisie to marry him.

"Why on earth not?"

"Well it's one thing to say she loves me—but she can't marry me without her parents' approval."

"You mean that if you were certain that Mr and Mrs Henderson would give you their blessing you could then pop the question to Maisie?"

"Yes, I suppose so."

"All right, you'd better go and see them."

"Oh no, no, I couldn't."

"Well you can't expect them to come to you."

"I couldn't face them and say 'I want to marry your daughter'."

"In that case you'd better write to them."

"Write asking if I can come and see them?"

"No. Write telling them you want to marry Maisie, and suggesting that you'll call for an answer later."

Charlie could hardly object to that. If they didn't approve of the marriage, they wouldn't see him. He told Maisie of the plan and she approved wholeheartedly. John dictated the letter and Charlie copied it out and delivered it.

The next day Maisie told Charlie that her parents wanted him to call at eleven.

John made sure Charlie was all spruced up and shining and packed him off.

Half an hour later, as John was shaving, Charlie returned. John was about to congratulate him, when Charlie said plaintively:

"I'm terribly sorry, Johnnie, but I didn't go in."

"Didn't go in?" he nearly cut himself.

"I couldn't. I couldn't—honestly."

"Why the blazes not? They expected you."

"I know, but the Sneddons' car was there—parked in front."

"Are you telling me that . . .? Oh for goodness sake, Charlieboy. . . . Go straight back there this minute."

"Oh, I can't. I feel such a fool."

"Well, you are a fool. Come on, you get in the car and I'll take you back."

"I can't. You haven't shaved."

"It doesn't matter. I'm not asking for Maisie's hand. Come on, get in the car!"

Charlie gave in—got in the car—and was driven to the Hendersons by John, still in his shirtsleeves and with his face half covered in lather. The Sneddons' car had gone, and Mrs Henderson was watching from the window. She opened the front door herself, fell on Charles's neck and kissed him, and John turned the car round and drove back satisfied that at last Charlie and he were both going to be married.

July 14th, 1921, was the date agreed for John's wedding. Had it taken place a year earlier, Muriel would have been thrilled and excited. Now she was only glad that the long wait at home was over, and that at last she'd be able to make a home for John. That was the one thing she knew he needed, and it was the one thing she felt sure she could provide. Their relationship had hardly changed since the day they became engaged. Physically and mentally they were still holding hands on top of Beachy Head. For both of them it was the practicalities of getting married which carried them forward, rather than the first wave of love.

The house they decided to rent was in the best part of Glasgow. It wasn't very big, but it was convenient to run, and it had a tennis court—essential for a young couple who wanted to lead any sort of social life during the summer. Muriel needn't worry about making friends, though. Half the people round were friends and relatives ot the Reiths. Nor need she worry over money—£1,200 a year, "not forgetting the bonus", as John reminded her, was a pretty good salary at a time when the miners were on strike for £3 a week. John didn't approve of the strike and thought the Government very weak and feeble to give in to their demands.

"And now they're flooding some of the pits. It's disastrous."

He was glad that Beardmore's was safe and sound and almost thriving, although there was a still a lot to be done. He'd be very busy for the next six months, reorganising the marketing side of the business—which was one of the reasons he had deliberately fixed on mid-July for the wedding. The other reason, as Muriel well knew, was Charlie.

John was still afraid that he'd lose Charlie once Muriel and he were married. No matter how often Muriel said that Charlie would always be welcome at the house, there were bound to be occasions. And what about running up to London for a weekend, or going to see a show, or climbing the Cairngorms or even going to the Western Club? Muriel would have to come first. Charlie was naturally so polite and considerate and self-effacing he would never force himself on Muriel. Moreover, he was still very fond of her, and Maisie might get jealous. Mind, she said she wasn't.

"I want you to know, John, that this will make no difference." Maisie held out her magnificent diamond engagement ring encrusted with pearls—'Sands to the Saharah', as John remarked *sotto voce* to Charlie. "I understand all about Charlie's relationship with you and Muriel. The only difference will be that now there will be four of us!"

She held her face up to give him the expected kiss. He refused it. John, as explained before, took kissing very seriously, and this would have been the kiss of Judas. He felt betrayed, not only by Maisie and Charlie, but by his own instincts. He should never have pushed Charlie into Maisie's arms. She was determined to become Mrs Bowser, and then Charlie would become Mrs Bowser's husband . . .

He went over to see Douglas and had a long frank talk with him. Douglas was reassuring.

"Nonsense. When I saw you and Charlie with Maisie at the Sneddons' christening party, I said to Ada I didn't know which

one of you Maisie was going to marry. She's half in love with
you already."

"So she should be," Ada piled it on. "If it hadn't been for you
she'd never have got Charlie."

The thought mortified John. He went over to the church for
the service. Douglas had asked him to read the lesson. Charlie
and Maisie had got there early and were already sitting in the
front pew—Maisie chattering away.

"Terribly sorry about Wednesday and Thursday. Grannie's
coming to stay and she wants to meet Charlie."

"Oh. Muriel'll be disappointed. She was hoping Charlie would
help choose the furniture."

"I'll see you off at the station," said Charlie.

John knew from his voice that he was really sorry not to be
coming to Whiteley's. They'd planned to see Pavlova as well.
John didn't care for the ballet, but Muriel and Charlie did. That's
why they all got on so well together—they complemented each
other. But Maisie wanted Charlie all for herself. She clasped his
hand as though he were desperately ill and might die at any
moment. "But you'll come with Charlie and me when we go to
choose our furniture? Promise?"

He'd no time to prepare his reading from the Old Testament. It
was all about the weak King Ahab completely dominated by his
wife Jezebel, and how Elijah tried to save him from her, and
finished up fleeing for his life. He didn't look at Maisie until he'd
closed the Bible. From that moment she was Jezebel in his mind
and henceforth in his conversation and in his diary. He'd always
avoided using her name up till then, as though by not writing it
she would go away and cease to exist. Now she would be
punished and vilified remorselessly.

Charlie saw them off at the station as promised. Muriel sat
patiently in the compartment. She wasn't happy, but she was
glad that John and Charlie were together, even briefly, as it made
John less irritable.

9

Everybody at Coatbridge was known to John by name. He'd made a point of this, from the start. Sir William Beardmore had been impressed. His knowledge hardly went beyond his Board of Directors.

"I suppose you got the idea from the Americans, eh?"

"No, sir—long before that. When I worked on the shop floor myself I was easily recognised on account of my height. But the other workers didn't suffer from the same affliction."

"Affliction? You mean being tall is an affliction?"

"Six feet-two is a good height, Sir William. Anything over that is an affliction." He went on. "One of the things the working man resents most is not having a name. 'Hey you, Jock!' isn't good enough. I knew everyone's name in my army unit, and at the Marine Depot too. And I know everybody here at Beardmore's."

John prided himself on man management. In the army he was popular with the men, but seldom with his fellow officers. The same thing at Beardmore's. The Board put up with him because they had to—the men actually liked him. His rigid discipline was softened by genuine sympathy and concern, and on occasions, money. Consequently they responded to the wedding by having a whip round unbeknown to John.

He was about to get into his car, en route for Brighton and the Odhams, when the Foreman stopped him. A moment later he was surrounded by his workforce and, standing on the office steps, given his wedding present. He was delighted and astonished. Charlie had warned him that something was in the air, but he never expected such generosity.

"Twelve fish forks, fruit knives and forks, and two silver toast

racks." He told Muriel with pride. "And that from men getting
two or three pounds a week. Then they drew the car like a
triumphal chariot through the main gates and covered me in
confetti! I hope I'm always worthy of such affection."

Muriel placed the fish knives in a prominent position with the
other gifts. She wanted people to see what sort of a man she was
marrying. Then they went to see the Vicar with Charlie, and after
that tea at the Homestead. Uncle William—W.J. Odhams had
been looking at the presents, and said he'd never had such gifts
from his workers. John took to Aunt Lottie who was so much
younger than Uncle William, though he looked old because of
his arthritis. He decided he liked his future in-laws except for his
father-in-law, mother-in-law and Edward. Jean had telephoned to
say that she and Mother had arrived at their Brighton hotel, so
Charlie and John went to make sure they were comfortable. By
the time they got back it was time for dinner, and Maisie had
joined them, plus Archie, and Douglas. The advance contingent
of the numerous Reiths threw John into a state of gloom, and he
went off to celebrate his last night of bachelordom with Charlie.

They walked in the garden and then sat on the beach talking.
They heard Maisie calling, but didn't answer. She'd been talking
at dinner, as though she already owned Charlie.

"This time tomorrow it'll all be over," said Charlie.

"As long as our friendship remains, that's all I care about."

"You care about Muriel, don't you?"

"Oh, yes. I want to get married, but I'm still worried about our
future friendship."

"We'll always be friends, John." Charlie said it with such
conviction that John knew he didn't mean it. The real Charlie
was always uncertain. That was Jezebel talking. John got up.

"Good heavens, it's eleven o'clock."

The sun had gone down on them, almost unnoticed.

John chose the lesson and Douglas read it well. The Vicar
obeyed most of John's minute instructions and the church was
properly prepared. There were no parish leaflets on the pews
such as had marred his father's funeral. He left the floral
arrangements to Mrs Odhams, but made sure that Muriel's

bouquet was plain white—carnations and white heather only. At least she would have all the Scottish luck going. She would need it, as he said in his speech after the ceremony.

Man and wife before God, they went into the vestry. Mother and Charlie signed the register, their voices subdued but the Vicar's loud. Then Muriel suddenly burst into tears. John did his best to comfort her, but he'd never seen her cry before and he couldn't understand and wasn't reassured when the Vicar said she was crying for joy. He lent her his handkerchief and Charlie held her hand.

At the reception Charlie's brother kept Jezebel happy by running after her with her coat wherever she went. She was dressed up to the nines and in John's opinion looked a fright. But for once he was grateful to Charlie's brother whom he disliked. Usually he had a nineteen-year-old girl in tow—half his age . . . by looking after Jezebel he enabled Charlie to do his duties as best man. When the bride had gone to put on her going away clothes, John and Charlie slipped upstairs with Douglas and said a prayer.

The happy couple were seen off at the station. Kisses and hugs all round, and John even included Jezebel. She protested her undying love for him and Muriel as usual. He didn't want her love, he wished her dead.

The Highlands of Scotland were beautiful, the weather perfect, and Muriel had at last got the man she loved alone to herself. She was content and happy.

John too was happy with the girl he loved, but he didn't consider that a honeymoon was an excuse to loaf around reading old magazines when the Cuillins behind the hotel beckoned them. However, Muriel was tired after the long journey, quite apart from the wedding celebrations, and John was totally averse to behaving like an ordinary newly wed. He stuck it for two days, writing long letters to Charlie and walking down to the village post office. Muriel agreed with him that Charlie had been a marvellous Best Man and that Maisie looked a fright, that Jean was a menace and that Beta was obviously suffering from iron deficiency but she didn't agree that he should write to the

Chairman of G.W.R. to complain at their having to share a
lavatory on the train. John was annoyed for Charlie's sake. "After
all the trouble he took to make sure we had a decent berth! I got
a note off to him from Euston, so he may do something."

Muriel began to realise that to make her husband happy, she
would not only have to be everything she was at the moment, but
everything Charlie had been in the past. On the third day,
therefore, when John had refused to linger over their breakfast
coffee, saying: "It's a pity to waste the best part of the day. If
Charlie'd been here, we'd have been up the Cuillins by now!"

Muriel got up from the table with a suddenness that surprised
him, ordered a pack lunch, and within half an hour they were
striding across the moors. When, five hours later, Muriel
staggered back to the hotel, she had covered eighteen miles.
Seven miles there and two up the mountain. The other guests
were astonished and full of admiration, and Muriel, relaxing in a
hot bath, hoped that she'd won her spurs. She didn't appreciate
that for the rest of her married life she'd have to keep proving
herself. However, John let her see what he'd put in the diary: "I
was glad Muriel had done so well". He was bringing it up to date
and had spent most of the evening at it.

"And don't forget, Musie, there'll be no Bluebeard's Chambers
in our house. You can read my diary any time you like."

She kissed him. She was so pleased that he trusted her
implicitly. "I'd rather not, thank you, John."

"Why not?"

"It might become a habit, and I'd be checking every day to see
what you'd been doing, and whether you'd mentioned me. Or
even whether you loved me."

"You may be right," was his non-committal response.

The next day they went on to Dunvegan Castle which had
been inhabited by the MacLeods for a thousand years. John read
the entire guide to Muriel and it began to rain. The rain
continued all the next day. It rained when they took the
Glencoe round the Islands. It rained and a storm came up when
they returned. Muriel was a good sailor, and John was able to
put another proud comment in the diary: "Muriel was the only
woman who wasn't sick".

Muriel was the right girl for him. He regarded himself as an infallible judge of character—it was one of his greatest assets. It was unthinkable that Muriel should be other than the perfect wife.

But honeymoon, for John, was synonymous with holiday, and holiday was synonymous with boredom. Walking round the loch hand in hand was no relaxation for a man who didn't want to relax, and whose mind was constantly occupied with thoughts of self-advancement and self-improvement. Muriel loved plants and seaweed and seashells and birds, and would have been quite content to sit and look at them. John saw the bits of waste paper fluttering on the edge of the tide, and wondered what the council were doing about it.

"Have you ever kept accounts?"

"No, John."

"How do you know how much you can afford to buy?"

"Well. . . When I run out I stop buying."

"But your income varies. I shall make you a housekeeping allowance with money for yourself, and that you'll have to account for. Do you know how to do that?"

"Oh, yes, I think so. Look at those seagulls—there must be a shoal of mackerel out there."

John decided to let the matter rest till the honeymoon was over. He would take a course in accounting, and then teach Muriel. Meanwhile he'd pay the bills himself. He wished they'd made their home in London. He didn't care for the South of England, but the capital city was the place for him—not Glasgow . . . He had to be at the nerve centre of the Empire . . . His career demanded it. What career? He must go back to London as soon as possible.

The next day it rained. "Musie, are you really enjoying your honeymoon?"

"Of course I am, John."

"Because I think it's a very overrated pastime. You're missing your friends. If we go back you can furnish the house, and make it your own. And I mean that—you can do what you like with it—so long as I have a desk and a cold bath . . . and a telephone," he added.

"But I like it here, John."

"Och, come on, we'll go back to the hotel and pack our bags. There's a train at 3.15."

"But I don't need friends so much when I've got you, John."

"Well, your friends miss you."

10

It was obvious to everyone except John, that his friendship with Charlie Bowser could not continue unchanged. Who was going to be the one to tell him? Muriel, as his wife, was unable to do so. She was well aware that she'd be instantly accused of disloyalty. "He who is not for me is against me" was the usual text quoted on such occasions. Mr and Mrs Bowser had always been "hopelessly against our friendship from the start!" (Regardless of the fact that it was Charlie's father who first suggested John's name to Sir William.) His mother couldn't be approached—she had enough troubles of her own with Jean's divorce proceedings, and Robert owing money to half the landladies in Scotland. Archie and Douglas would only be older brothers poking their noses in, and Jean was an unspeakable virago trying to ruin his relationship with everyone he held dear, including his mother.

They were all agreed on one thing, though, that the longer John went on trying to live in his dream world, the walls of which were already breached, the more desperate he was becoming. The worse would be the awakening, and the more bitter the disillusion.

There was only one person who could speak and be listened to—Charlie. And Charlie was still partly in the dream world himself, half in love with Muriel, and hoping that somehow or other Maisie would allow him to continue the friendship which had, for the past eight years, completely dominated his life. Had he been honest with himself, he would have admitted that he wanted to be free—free from John and free from Maisie. He wanted to go abroad and see the world—China or America. Once he was married to Maisie he'd probably finish up as a

country gentleman, living on her 1500 acres. There were already
dark rumblings from John on the subject, as he saw his Assistant
becoming less and less interested in the routine at Beardmore's.

Maisie, like many another loving wife, including Jezebel, had
an overwhelming instinct for self-preservation. If that meant
driving a nail through the head of her rival, so be it. Yet never
for one moment would she have thought herself capable of such
a deed. She regarded herself as a kind and soft person, which
she was. John made no concessions to anyone. He never paused
long enough to stop himself making a remark, however hurtful.
If he ever had a regret, it was regret that a much more hurtful
remark had occurred to him later which he might have said at
the time! He was like a floundering shark, caught in the shallows,
snapping at any hand that might try to feed him, longing for
revenge and longing to be back in the sea where he could once
more be the master of himself and his environment.

John had one other friend—Thomas Loudon, school friend of
the Glasgow Academy days and also his accountant. He was
loyal and constant, and being an accountant, was generally
referred to as "Poor Loudon". "Poor Loudon wants to have lunch
with me—Poor Loudon sent some flowers to Mother—Poor
Loudon met me at my club . . .". But he was a good listener. He
hadn't seen John since April and was dismayed to find his friend
in a state of mind which almost amounted to paranoia. John
poured out his anger and frustration.

"The insensitivity of that girl beats everything. I invited
Charles round the day we got the furniture in—our first visitor.
And who's he got with him? That girl!" Loudon noticed that he
never used Maisie's name if he could avoid it. "And again last
week—after Charlie and I had been through hell and high water
at Coatbridge getting the accounts passed by the Board—I asked
Charlie to come back for tea. He said he'd just pop home first.
When he came, that girl was with him. I stayed in my room for
three-quarters of an hour, and when I came down I said nothing.
We had tea and that girl got up and said she had to go and see
an aunt or something. So I said 'That's all right. Charlie can stay
here.' 'Who's going to drive me there?' she says. Couldn't walk,
Oh no! Charlie followed her like a tame dog. I said to him in the

hall, 'Well, see you Saturday and Sunday,' and all he said was, 'I doubt it.' I doubt it!"

He started walking about. Loudon pulled his legs in as John swept past him.

"She's jealous. I've known Charlie eight years and she hasn't known him for eight months. He daren't show any affection, and that's on his conscience, so he won't even discuss the subject. I said to him yesterday, 'She's got you like a rat in a trap! She's nothing but a sentimental servant girl!' How a chap like Bowser could fall for a girl like that—he told me he'd rather spend a weekend with his future in-laws at "Argaty"—he made the house sound like a cheap brand of margarine—rather than go climbing with me in the Cairngorms! Can you credit it? Even when he goes to church—doesn't matter where it is—he's always got that . . . Jezebel with him!"

Loudon said nothing. He realised that John wasn't talking to him. He was merely repeating his thoughts out loud. Thoughts that were chasing round and round, like demons relentlessly pursuing him to the Shades. There was nothing Loudon could say or do to help his friend.

As though reading his thoughts, John said, "I'm like a man possessed, Loudon. And I'm fearful that when—if—Charlie Bowser is exorcised from my mind, my happiness and my love will be driven out at the same time."

Loudon got up to leave. He picked up his brief-case.

"Don't go," John said. "Musie'll be back at ten. She's gone to a dance in Dunblane." His manner was quite normal again.

"No, no, I must get home," said Loudon with a perfunctory handshake.

John returned to his study and got out his diary. But it wasn't for 1920, it was for 1913. He read: "I really am ridiculously fond of this schoolboy. But I feel I can help him perhaps."

He was still sitting there when Muriel came in from the dance. She was with Doris, her cousin. She was flushed and happy. "Well," she said, giving him a kiss on the top of his head, "did Mr Loudon sort out the income tax?"

"Income tax? Er, no."

He'd forgotten that that was why he'd asked Loudon to call.

On the anniversary of his father's death, John went over to look at the new headstone.

> 53 years Minister of College and Kelvingrove Church, Moderator of the U.F. Church of Scotland 1914.
> Died December 13th 1919.
> They shall see his face.

He said a prayer and remembered his dream of carrying his father and walking him to church. On the way back he bought a book on the symbolism of dreams. If he didn't like it he could always give it to someone he didn't like for Christmas.

On New Year's Eve Beth died. It had been expected, but not so soon. John was overcome with grief, but Muriel comforted him. She'd scarcely ever met Beth except at the wedding. Now she heard how much Beth had always meant to John. How she'd played with him for long hours in the nursery and protected him from the elder children, and how she had broken free from the stifling atmosphere of the Manse to become a nurse. He blamed Jean for disrupting the household and making it impossible for Beth to remain. He'd given the book on dreams to Beth for Christmas.

Charlie was at the funeral. They stood beside each other at the graveside, and he wondered how he'd feel when he stood next to Charlie in a few months time as his Best Man. How he would be able to endure the moment when he had to take the ring from his pocket and hand it to Charlie to put on Jezebel's finger and make him hers forever? If 1920 had gone from happiness and love to a bitter lament, 1921 was certainly starting off the other way round.

The next blow came three weeks later. Sir William came into his office with a letter in his hand.

"You know anything about this, Reith?"

He gave John the letter. John read it and handed it back. Charlie had tendered his resignation.

"No, sir. But I knew there was a possibility."

"You never mentioned it." Sir William had grown so used to John's almost uncanny knack of being one step ahead of the

Board that he felt let down on this occasion.

"When I said I knew of the possibility, I meant that with 1,500 acres and £20,000 to play with, Mr Bowser might not need a job with us, sir."

"All the same . . ."

"I suggest we combine his farewell presentation with his wedding present."

"Good idea. I'll leave it to you. You know the sort of thing he likes."

He went back to his office grateful that his General Manager would, as usual, take care of everything. John was not grateful for the confidence now placed in him by the directors. He expected it. He was profoundly irritated by the lack of concern shown by the Chairman, at the resignation of an efficient and well-nigh irreplaceable member of the staff. He wondered how much longer he could go on working for a company who cared so little about anything except profit and loss.

John re-read the letter. The hand was that of Charlie, but the voice was the voice of Jezebel. One by one she was cutting the ties which bound Charlie to him. The *coup de grace* would be delivered on the Wedding Day. John prepared himself for it with mounting dread. He could hardly bring himself to go to church to hear the banns being read out. He went alone in his capacity as Best Man, and sat thinking what he should give Charlie as a wedding present. Whatever it was, Jezebel would probably duplicate it as she had done his other presents. On Charlie's last birthday Jezebel had given him a silver matchbox to hang on his chain, knowing full well that John had already given him a gold one. She'd done the same thing with a ring, and would probably give him a gold wrist-watch next. His fury mounted. How dare she trivialise the gifts of friendship into mere trinkets to be bought and sold?

"I publish the bann of marriage between . . ."

He thought of the hundreds of times he and Charlie had attended Communion together. That surely must still have meaning for his friend. He was supposed to go straight home to Muriel. He wanted to see Charlie, talk to him, listen to him. He'd got a book he was reading called *Simon called Peter*. He'd brought it with him to read during the sermon. There was some good stuff in it that he'd like to read to Charlie. He went to Charlie's flat in Lancaster Crescent.

He was cautiously welcomed, Charlie making it clear that he had to go home for Sunday Lunch.

"That's fine. We've got two hours," said John.

In the past the two hours would have been overflowing with talk—now there were silences. Not empty silences, but silences filled with unspoken messages. John was reminded of his father after he'd had his stroke, understanding what was said, but unable to reply. He understood what Charlie never said, could not bring himself to say—"It's over. The past is past and gone."

"Have you got the list of wedding guests?" he asked.

"Yes, There aren't very many I'm afraid."

"I've been reading this book—there's some good stuff in it."

"Is there?" Charlie looked inside the dust jacket.

"Here, I've marked one or two passages. I'll read one to you if you like."

"Oh, thank you."

Charlie appeared relieved to be able to sit back in his chair without having to make conversation.

John must have been reading for half an hour, maybe longer when he heard again that odd choking sound that Charlie had made when John was chattering on about Muriel. He stopped in mid-sentence. Charlie was standing over him. He wrested the book out of John's hands and hurled it through the window.

John didn't move. He said, "I'll pick it up on the way home." He pushed his chair back and got up. Charlie was still motionless by the window. "They're making a farewell presentation on the office steps tomorrow, by the way. It's meant to be a surprise, but I thought I'd better warn you."

"Will I have to make a speech?"

Charlie came to. He hated speaking in public, his knees always went to jelly. John felt in his breast pocket and pulled out a piece of paper.

"I've roughed out something for you, Charlieboy."

Charlie took it. "Thanks."

John got as far as the door. "I take it I'm still your Best Man?"

"Yes, of course. Sorry about the book."

"I hope the wedding present I'm giving you doesn't suffer a similar fate. You'll see from your speech the men are giving you the inevitable fish knives."

Charlie gave him the sort of half-smile that had so often signified contriteness and heralded forgiveness. John couldn't bring himself to make the smallest gesture. The shadow of Jezebel was between them. Even if he stepped over it, it would still be there.

"See you at the office tomorrow. The presentation'll be at 4.45. Don't be late."

"No, no, of course not."

Still John hovered by the door. "Oh by the way, so that you don't get two of a kind—what's . . . she giving you for a wedding present?"

"A gold wrist-watch. Rolex Oyster. We chose it together."

"I'll try and think of something you haven't already got."

11

Apart from the presentation ceremony John saw nothing more of Charlie until the wedding. He bumped into Jezebel in the street one day. She expressed delight at seeing him and took his arm and walked with him. She said she and Charlie were determined to remain just the same as ever—whatever that meant—and that they were going to buy a house in Dunblane too! They'd all be together, wouldn't that be fun? And she thanked him effusively for writing Charlie's speech at the presentation, and she didn't know how he'd ever get through his speech at the wedding when he'd have to do it all by himself! (So that was the point—in case John thought he was going to write it!)

"We don't want a great big 'do' like you and Muriel had. It'll only be family and real friends."

They parted, Jezebel most unwillingly, giving him three little kisses as though she didn't trust herself with one big one. He felt she was having a good look to see into which temple she would drive the nail. Presumably that would take place after the wedding.

She came running back. "Oh, by the way—I nearly forgot. Charlie says he's not having any bachelor party. He wants to stop at home and be quiet." She turned and ran back to her chauffeur-driven car, waving as she passed him. He lifted his umbrella without looking in her direction.

Next day he resigned from Beardmore's.

When he broke the news to Muriel she was so shocked she burst into tears and ran out of the room.

She was rarely if ever taken by surprise again. She learned to read the signs. Small decisions could be reached after a walk in

the garden, holding hands. But the big ones, involving inner
turmoil, were always preceded by prolonged withdrawals to the
study and general gloom. Occasionally there were acid remarks
to test her steel, or outbursts of temper to reduce her to tears,
but otherwise she was left alone. Then one day she would return
from shopping to find the furniture had been moved around—in
the study as a rule—and the decision taken.

With hindsight, therefore, it was obvious that John was about
to change his way of life when he'd suddenly decided to move his
new study to a bedroom upstairs, where he could get more sun
and see the garden. The ideal room would have been the spare
bedroom—the nicest room in the house. But it was kept almost
totally unused and inviolate for Mother. It was hardly likely that
Mrs Reith would want to come and stay very often, as she was
not to far away in Dumfries, but the room was Mother's and must
remain so.

John went after Muriel, sat on the bed, and explained patiently
why he couldn't bear to stay any longer at Beardmore's. "I've
done all I can, I've shot my bolt. Whatever I managed to do now
would only be improving on what's gone before. That's all right
for a middle aged man who wants to keep his wife and family
and then retire on a pension, but my future lies in front of me
not behind. I've got forty years."

"Have you been offered something else?"

"No. I've only this minute resigned. I'll leave as soon as
they've found someone else. They may not even bother to
replace me. They haven't even thought of replacing Charlie."

"But supposing you don't get another job?"

"That's one of the most stupid things you've ever said to me. I
shall get a job, but I doubt if it will be in Scotland."

"Why not?"

"Because I've had enough of being a cog in the industrial
wheel. I'm tired of being manipulated by my job. The most
exciting event in my life is to produce a new taxi which will turn
in its own length! My father would turn in his grave if he
thought that was the sum total of my ambition."

Muriel leaned back on the pillow. She longed for him to take
her in his arms.

John got up. "And there's another reason for going to live in
London. . ."

"London? You never said we were going to live in London!"

"It's the centre of the world, Musie. That's where I belong.
That's my destiny. Not ekeing out my life in Dunblane. And I'll
tell you another thing—you know that redbrick monstrosity up
the road? You know who's bought it?"

Muriel knew without being told—his tone was so furious.
"Charlie and Maisie?"

"None other. Mr and Mrs Bowser and twelve bedrooms! Trust
her to chose the ugliest house in Britain!"

So that was it—and that was that.

Maisie and Charlie were married in Dunblane Cathedral. There
were hardly any guests, and Mrs Reith and Jean insisted on
sitting at the back behind a pillar. John left his seat in the front
row to try and persuade them to move up and help swell the
numbers, but they refused to budge and he returned fuming.
Charlie said nothing. It was hardly the job of the bridegroom to
soothe the feelings of the Best Man.

John was uneasy and fidgety. The moment he'd agonised over
for months had arrived. He didn't know whether he'd be able to
go through with it. He thought the worst moment would be
when Charlie put the ring on Jezebel's finger. He was gazing at a
memorial to his right. He resolved to do the same when the
clergyman pronounced them man and wife.

But that moment was not the worst, nor was signing the
register. It was watching Charlie and Maisie walking slowly
down the aisle to *The Wedding March*. It seemed to him then that
Charlie was walking out of his life. He was so unutterably
desolate that he couldn't go to the reception. He told Muriel to
go and he'd follow: he had to tip the organist.

He went home and sat alone in his study. It seemed to him
that God had definitely been on the other side. For over a year
everything had gone wrong—his father'd died, his best loved
sister, and now his best friend. He got down his diary, opened it
at a clean page and put the date on it. He wrote: "My beloved
friend of nearly ten years fell sick of grievous poisoning on

26.6.21, and died 3.3.22." He should have added—"Thank God I've still got Muriel", but he didn't.

To be out of work was a totally new experience for John Reith, and he didn't like it. He'd taken to reading the odd book of psychiatry in the hopes of gaining a better understanding of other people rather than himself.

"You see Musie, I am not a truly creative person. I can't spend my life writing and playing the piano, though I can do both. I cannot exist without working at something."

"Why don't we take a holiday?" It was only two weeks since he'd left Beardmore's. "Write some letters off to people you know telling them you're looking for a job and there's bound to be something waiting for you when we get back."

He did as she suggested and they had a glorious holiday in Guernsey. At least the weather was glorious and Muriel got sunburned, but John, lying on the beach in between jumping off rocks into deep water to frighten her and collecting fern roots to send to his mother-in-law, worried about his future.

The hall table was stacked with letters on their return. Everyone was "quite sure you'll soon be hard at it again", but nobody actually offered employment.

"Never mind," said Muriel, "we'll go and see Uncle William. He knows no end of people."

"I'm not going to make use of your family, Muriel."

"They won't mind a bit."

"No. And that's final. Would you say I was overbearing and tyrannical?" He was reading another letter.

"No, of course not. Not in the least."

"Well Mrs Bowser does: 'Dear John, I just want to thank you for all you've done for Charlie. As you know, I didn't care for your mutual friendship, as it caused dissention in the family. Charlie was often very unhappy about it because you were so tyrannical and overbearing, and altogether the past ten years have been a very difficult time for me too. However, the chapter is now closed with, I hope, no ill-feelings on either side.' She always was the martyred type."

He went up to his study and methodically replied to every

letter. He could never bear to have an unanswered letter on his desk or an unpaid bill—even when out of work.

He made several visits to London to attend interviews, but May became June and June July and July August, and still no work. He went to Saint Martin's in the Fields for the first time and was inspired by the sermon to write to Muriel: "It doesn't matter if the mountain doesn't move if we believe it will move. When I am in Scotland I feel there is nothing going on but tea and tennis and that that's all I'm fit for. But here in the capital of the Empire, I am conscious of abilities which almost overwhelm me. I am as eager to pass on the fires of Inspiration from pew or pulpit or printed page which burn within me."

Muriel wondered what fires of inspiration he was going to pass on to her when he got back. She was actually the guinea pig. She wasn't doing very well at accountancy, and dreaded him going through the books with her. She didn't take the remarks about tea and tennis too seriously. John enjoyed both. They were members of the club and John spent a lot of time down there. He was a great favourite with the ladies—particularly the younger ones who enjoyed his droll sense of humour and old world good manners. The Twenties had even reached Scotland, and there was a freedom between the sexes unknown since the time of Rabbie Burns and unheard of in the Manse at Kelvingrove. John entered into the spirit of the game which meant no more to him than "Postman's Knock".

"That's all it is, Musie—Postman's Knock."

"If that's all it is, why's everyone talking about you and Nora Wilson?"

"Well, what harm is there in an occasional kiss over the garden gate?"

"None, if that's where it stops."

She was miserable and upset. She couldn't understand why he should even think of kissing and carrying on with another girl when they'd hardly been married a year. Ada and Douglas made a few feeble attempts to help by bringing the subject round to "marital relations" and Douglas said jocularly that he'd given a hundred to one John would never take Nora Wilson to a dance. Even Muriel laughed at that because John said, "Only because

I'm no good at dancing." He didn't mention that Nora had said he was no good at kissing and didn't know how to do it! He decided to be more loving to Muriel, but continued to see Nora and to kiss her, and he noted in his diary that he'd hardly thought of Charlie since Nora came on the scene. "But perhaps the cure is worse than the disease!"

Still no sign of a job, though his old contacts like Mr Bowser tried their best. There was an American friend from wartime days in Philadelphia who suddenly wrote asking him to come out and work for him, but the ink on John's reply was still wet when a second communication arrived informing him that his friend had died. But disappointing though all this was, monotonous and unproductive, John could still cling to his self-respect because he never really wanted the jobs as such, he only wanted the money they could bring to enable him to support Muriel and his Mother. When the day came that he was turned down for a job he'd set his heart on—that'd be a different story.

For a man of twenty, or even twenty-five, to write in his private diary that he was certain that he would be in the Cabinet in ten years, and that his destiny was not to die in a sea of mud but to become someone great, is not so very unusual. But for a man of thirty-three without money or influence or higher education—without even a job—to talk of his "destiny being fulfilled" makes him either Hitler or Jesus Christ. John Reith was a cross between them, and like them, a late developer.

Sir William Bull was a Conservative M.P. who liked and admired Lloyd George, even though he was a Liberal. He therefore didn't hold John's politics against him when he interviewed him for the temporary job of honorary political secretary to him. Together with recommendations from the Headmaster of Greshams—John's old public school—he had the assurance of W.J. Odhams that John knew no more of politics than he did of good wine, and could therefore be thoroughly relied upon to remain sober and keep his head during political in-fighting when "all around were losing theirs". Sir William needed nobody's recommendation to see at a glance that John was an unusually intelligent young man, not in the least overawed by Sir William's length of service or superior know-

ledge. When he got to know his new secretary better he saw that
John, like Lloyd George, had appealed to him because he was a
man with an ability to manage others, and to grasp and absorb
facts and figures within seconds.

John had for some months previously been trying to "get into
politics". He'd written to various politicians and had armed
himself with a formidable wealth of knowledge about the current
issues of the day at home and abroad, the attitudes of the various
parties and so on. He'd had no luck in getting adopted as a
prospective candidate, but he already knew who was who in the
corridors of power. On the other hand he didn't know enough to
have a worthwhile opinion. That, and his proven powers of
leadership and organisation clinched it as far as Sir William was
concerned. John was happy to take on the job because he had
nothing else to do. A year of enforced idleness had made him
less fussy about the terms of employment—there was no talk of a
bonus! And as Sir William pointed out, the post amounted to
being Secretary to the London Unionist Members of Parliament
who met fortnightly while the House was sitting. It would bring
John into contact with many of the most important people in
government. It would be valuable experience and could well
lead to other things.

Sir William made sure it did. Within a week of starting his new
job, John was shown an advertisement for another. Sir William
had a financial interest in wireless—marketing radios. A new
company had just been set up to provide programmes, run by
his friend Sir William Noble.

"They want a General Manager—sounds rather your line. The
job doesn't start till the end of December, by which time the fate
of the Government will be decided, and you will be once more
foot loose."

"I'll apply. Shall I mention your name?"

"Certainly. If they want a reference I'll give it with pleasure.
Go round to your club now, and write a good letter."

"Thank you, sir."

He was grateful to Sir William. He was old enough to be his
father, and John rather liked him behaving as such.

"And don't think I'm only doing you a good turn. Sir William

Noble should be highly delighted. See you at the meeting." As
an afterthought he handed John a magazine. "You'd better take
this with you—it's on the back page."

Comfortably seated in the writing room at the Cavendish
Club, John read the advertisement over again. It was in the
"Appointments Vacant" column of *The Electrician*:

> "Applications are invited for the following offices:
> General Manager,
> Director of Programmes,
> Chief Engineer,
> Secretary.
>
> Only applicants with first class qualifications need apply.
> Applications to be addressed to Sir William Noble, Chairman of
> the Broadcasting Committee, Magnet House, Kingsway, W.C.2."

He quickly wrote his application on Club notepaper and
dropped it in the letter-box there. Then he thought he'd better
look up Sir William Noble in *Who's Who*. He discovered, to his
delight, that he was a churchman who would probably have
known his father, especially as he too was an Aberdonian. He
remembered when he first joined the Scottish Rifles in 1914, his
relations with his C.O. improved immediately when he said he
was the son of George Reith. He hurried back to the desk, and
got the hall porter to open the letter box. He retrieved his
application and added a postscript. "I too am an Aberdonian. No
doubt you knew my people." He sealed the envelope, put it back
in the box, gave the porter sixpence for his trouble, and hurried
off to his first meeting.

Lord Birkenhead's dining room was a lovely room, lined with
books and beautiful pictures. He was at the height of his powers
at the Bar and in politics. Much the same could be said of the
other politicians to whom John was introduced—Lloyd George
was still Prime Minister, Austen Chamberlain, the uncrowned
leader of the Conservatives—the others had all held Cabinet
office at one time or another. John kept silent, taking unobtrusive

notes, and absorbing the atmosphere. He'd always said he'd be
in the Cabinet by the time he was thirty-five. Well, here he was,
and if these men had their way, they would form the nucleus of
a Liberal Conservative Coalition Government after the coming
election.

Birkenhead, wearing tweeds and a red tie, and white carnation,
paced up and down as though expounding to the jury. When he
was on his feet, others had to listen. Over the next few weeks
John became accustomed to the same scene repeated over and
over again—in the committee rooms of the House of Commons,
in country houses and theatres up and down the country. The
message they wanted to drive home to their supporters inside
and outside the House was that the Socialists could only be
defeated if Liberals and Conservatives joined forces.

John spent most of his time organising their meetings for
them, with Sir William in the Chair. These cost money, a great
deal of money, but it was never in short supply, and he got quite
used to shelling out thousands of pounds in all directions. He
wrote to his mother: "I've learned more about the machinations
and skulduggery of politics in five days than father knew all his
life. I'm not so keen on a seat in the Cabinet as I was, but I
daresay if Chamberlain gets in I could get one."

Chamberlain didn't, nor did Lloyd George. Bonar Law did. By
rallying the disaffected Liberals and faithful Conservatives to his
side, he knocked people like Winston Churchill right out of the
ring, and the Liberal Party was on its knees.

John, though a Liberal himself, was unperturbed by the result.
He felt he'd been pushed in at the deep end of politics, had
swum around for a time, and come out unscathed. He knew very
well that he hadn't been called upon to "do" anything special—
he'd made no momentous suggestions or decisions—but he had
proved to himself that when it came to ability and brains and
sheer hard work he could hold his own with men of the calibre
of Birkenhead, Churchill and Lloyd George. When the day came
for his interview with the Broadcasting Committee, December
13th, 1922, he walked in at the front door of Magnet House,
Kingsway with all the confidence of a Man of Destiny.

That day was also the anniversary of his father's death.

"Mind you," he told Muriel later, "the fact that Sir William Noble greeted me like an old friend, and seemed to regard my appointment as a foregone conclusion, didn't exactly . . . lower my morale."

Nevertheless there were five more days to wait before the Board would "let him know". Nobody, however confident can be 100 per cent certain that he'll definitely win the race—there were over fifty other competitors, though only the short list of six were in the final.

John attended the winding-up meeting of the erstwhile Coalition Party, but he didn't surrender the keys of office. Sir William Bull was not only his friend and mentor, but he had the ear of Sir William Noble and remained a power behind the scenes. John was utterly determined to get the job.

Nevertheless, he decided to shut up the office, and take himself for a walk in St. James's park. He had no idea how he intended to pass the next few days, except that he wasn't going back to Scotland. He'd rung up Muriel and told her so. In fact he'd told her that if he did get the job, he'd probably be too busy to go home for Christmas, and if he didn't—too miserable. Poor Muriel, she must be a bit disappointed. He'd go home if he got the job, he'd write and tell her.

He was sitting on a park bench wondering what to do next, when a little boy came past. He heard a voice telling him not to run, and to his surprise found Archie coming towards him with a young woman. He hadn't seen Archie since Beth's funeral, and there was a warm exchange of greetings.

"And this is Mrs Burton, who's very kindly helping us at the Vicarage."

John was introduced to her and shook her hand politely. He didn't take to her. "Slovenly looking creature" is how he described her to Muriel when he wrote: "Archie and I had a long talk and he invited me to come back with him to the Vicarage. So here I am for the weekend, feeling rather guilty as it's my first visit for 4½ years! Nothing's changed, it's still as poor and dingey as ever. The war widow's a sort of companion help—that's what he calls her, anyway, and he likes children—pity he never had any. I read the lesson this morning. He has far too much to do

and doesn't look very well. He has services at 8, 11, 3, 4, and 7. I
feel sorry for him. I shall try and come home for Christmas, but I
can't say when. Expect me when you see me."

He liked giving a surprise. He liked to see the faces of the
people he loved light up. He liked that he could come home at
any time, the Prodigal Son, and be sure of a welcome. It was a
game he loved to play with his parents particularly. He'd turn up
without warning and there they'd be doing what they always did
at that hour—unchanging, unchangeable.

On December 20th he received a phone call at the Club. It was
Sir William Noble.

"Hullo, Reith. You'll be glad to know that the Board would like
you to become their first General Manager, and the decision was
unanimous. Congratulations."

"Thank you, sir."

"We'd very much appreciate it if you could come over as soon
as possible to discuss the financial aspect of the business and
your own salary and so on. Three o'clock suit you?"

"Yes. Yes, thank you, sir."

He put the phone down with a sense of overwhelming relief.
He thanked God with all his heart. Yet he wasn't going to sell
himself cheap. £2,000 plus annual bonus was the salary he
wanted. After all, he wasn't merely taking over the General
Managership of some thriving concern, or even non-thriving
one. The British Broadcasting Company only existed on paper.
They'd need new offices and studios and a complete workforce.

He sat down and wrote a Christmas card to Charlie. "Dear
Charlie, I wish you the best birthday you ever had, and I'm sure
it will be so. I also wish you every possible happiness at
Christmas and the New Year, and all prosperity. As always,
John."

He didn't mention the new job—he'd tell him about that later.
Meanwhile . . . he posted the card on his way to meet his Board
of Directors.

The six men who sat round the table with Sir William Noble
welcomed their new General Manager. They considered themselves very fortunate to have been able to obtain the services of

someone so highly recommended and suitable, and qualified etcetera. But they pointed out that they were not in business to risk their money.

"We're only a small limited private company with no resources. We're directly financed by the following companies."

Sir William read out a list of electrical manufacturers.

"They're taking a gamble—we're all taking a gamble." He smiled round at the Board who nodded their heads vigorously. "But we want it to be a small gamble. Offices, expenditure and staff must be kept to the minimum."

"And studios?" asked John faintly.

"Oh, we've got a studio, and a programme manager and an assistant and, from today, a Chief Engineer. So that side's taken care of for the moment. The terms of our licence are such that expansion will have to be fairly rapid." He pushed a wad of papers across the table. "But we must at all times keep pace with the sale of our wirelesses and radio equipment. I hope I've made that clear."

John gave an emphatic nod. He knew what was coming.

"So, as regards your salary, I'm afraid we can only offer you £1,750 per annum. And that is the maximum."

"I accept that, sir."

"Good. Then I suggest you start in earnest after Christmas and it only remains to fix our next Board Meeting . . ."

On his way out, John made the acquaintance of Arthur Burrows who was in charge of Programmes, and his assistant, C.A. Lewis, and said he looked forward to seeing them on the 30th and they exchanged addresses and telephone numbers. They both seemed pleasant enough at a first glance. John was disconcerted, however, to learn that the Chief Engineer was unsure whether he wanted the job after all.

"I'm not happy about the set up here. It means me leaving a good job with security and prospects. This seems to me altogether too precarious. I'm going to climb out while I'm safe."

John let him go without demur. It was a principle with him never to try and keep anyone who didn't want to stay. He'd find another Chief Engineer after Christmas. But he wondered a little. If the company seemed too precarious for the Chief Engineer,

how safe was it for a General Manager? He dismissed the
thought immediately. John Reith would see to it that the British
Broadcasting Company stayed well and truly in business. In any
case he'd got nowhere to climb back to.

He came out of Magnet House and walked down the Strand.
Quite suddenly Christmas and New Year was something he
wanted. He'd spend two more days in London, seeing the shows
and shopping and going to church. He loved the Christmas
hymns, the music of *The Messiah*, and all the Christmas decorations that he didn't get in Scotland.

He didn't tell Muriel the news of his new job, he didn't warn
her he was coming home. He caught the train from Euston and
travelled up with all the other Scots expatriots. The train was late
and by the time he reached Dunblane the town had gone to bed.
The front door was locked, but the lights were on, and he walked
round to the back of the house. It too was locked and there was
no answer when he knocked. He went back to the front door,
half afraid that the house was empty, that Muriel had gone out,
maybe even gone home to Southwick. He cursed his silliness in
not telling her he was coming.

He put down his parcels and suitcase on the top step and rang
the front doorbell and knocked thunderously. At last the door
opened. It was Musie, just about to go to bed, alone on
Christmas Eve. He took her in his arms and thought he'd never
been so happy in his life.

Next morning, Christmas Day, he got up early and walked
round the garden in his pyjamas.

12

The five days over Christmas passed so happily that Muriel
almost held her breath in case she did anything to spoil it. John
was his old self again. The weather was bright and sunny on the
heavy frost, and they went for walks over the Grampian Hills,
and in the evening sat reading by a good fire. John had laid in a
stock of wood, and constantly replenished the pile of dry logs in
the box. Even the arrival of a re-addressed Christmas card from
Charlie didn't disturb their happiness. It contained his reply to
John's best wishes: "Dear John, Please accept my thanks for your
card. The wishes thereon are most heartily reciprocated. Yours
Sincerely, D.C. Bowser."

He handed it to Muriel with the comment. "Smug little cad.
1923 could be as good a year for him as it will be for us."

"In what way, John?" She waited for the expected put down
and then the hurried exit and door slamming that would mean
the end of her short-lived happiness.

"He could have been my assistant of course—Assistant General Manager of the B.B.C.. Well, he won't be now." He put the
card up on the mantelpiece. "Now or ever."

If he was about to have second thoughts, they were put out of
his mind by the arrival of a telegram from Arthur Burrows,
asking him to break his journey at Newcastle, and take a look
round the new Station. John had no idea what was meant by
Station, but wired back that he'd do as he was asked.

"It means getting up at the crack of dawn," he told Muriel.

"You always do."

"Nevertheless there are times . . ." He sang. "Oh it's nice to get
up in the morning, but it's nicer to stay in bed." He put his arms
round her.

Muriel was up at five-thirty to see him off. She padded about quietly so as not to disturb Winnie the maid and they had breakfast in front of the roaring fire John had got going in the study. It was still dark outside, and snowing.

"Do you know, Musie, I'm sorry to be leaving my home."

"You'll be back at the weekends, surely?"

"Occasionally. From now on 'home' will be London. As soon as I can find a decent place to live, we'll move down there. . . for good."

Muriel had only just settled in Dunblane and had no wish to be uprooted in the middle of winter. She said warily: "You really think this job is 'the one' John?"

"This job is not only 'the one' for me, Musie, I'm the one for it."

He said it with such conviction that Muriel gave her approval with a kiss and said: "You'll make something of it, I know."

"It'll make something of me," he replied pedantically. "And us?" he added.

Two hours later, when confronted by the so-called Newcastle Wireless Station, he was considerably less sanguine. It was in a garage, on the back of a lorry. Tom Payne, the newly-appointed announcer-cum-Station-Director explained. "The apparatus broke down in our Eldon Square Studio on Christmas Eve. Someone or other in London had said we were going to open then, so we rushed round here and slung an aerial from the Co-op chimney. Didn't want to disappoint our crystal set public."

John looked up and there at the top of a high chimney was the B.B.C's latest technical advance. Payne went on: "I made the announcement, then I gave a violin recital."

"In the open air?"

"Yes. Miss May Osborne sang, and Mr Griffiths played the cello, and one or other of us held the microphone as near as possible to the solo instrument."

"Well, thank you, Mr Payne. I shall report back to Arthur Burrows that you're producing programmes and have had no complaints so far."

"Yes. Tell him our main problem now is some dog in a back yard that keeps howling as soon as we start."

John laughed. He still knew virtually nothing about the techni-
calities of broadcasting, but he was amused by the sense of fun
and adventure which seemed to pervade the wireless world. He
was reminded of his army days when he'd get his Engineers to
make something out of nothing in the front line. "So long as it
works, that's all that matters for the moment," was his dictum.
He was glad to be back in the trenches.

He shook hands with Payne, and wished him luck and told
him that in a day or two a new Chief Engineer would be
appointed, and that meanwhile, if he had any problems he was
to "ring my office and ask for Reith". Payne heaved a sigh of
relief. John gave the confident impression that he was General
Manager of a large and powerful organisation with offices "in the
City". In fact, the B.B.C. had been lent a single room in the
General Electric Company building, and the General Manager of
the B.B.C. didn't even have an office.

Next morning, Saturday, December 30th 1922, John left the
Cavendish Club at 8.30 and walked down Piccadilly and up the
Strand. It was cold and windy, and the Christmas-laden shops
were already open for business. He noted that there was a new
play opening at the "Aldwych" conveniently close to his office.
He reached the other end of Kingsway. Magnet House was
opposite to him—an unprepossessing office block with a red
brick Victorian facade. He crossed the road and entered to be
greeted by the liftman.

"I'm looking for the British Broadcasting Company."

"Third floor, sir. But there's nobody in yet."

"That's no bother. I'm the General Manager. My name's Reith,
what's yours?"

"Kilroy, sir."

The lift clanked upwards. Kilroy was not a small man, but his
eyes were only level with the General Manager's top pocket
handkerchief.

"You're Irish, aren't you. Were you in the war?"

"Oh yes, sir. Irish Fusiliers—biggest mistake of my life." He
pulled the lift gate back and led John down the passage, then
showed him into an office.

John looked round at the cluttered room—a couple of desks,

typewriters and wastepaper baskets. "Whose office is this?"

"Mr Burrows, Mr Lewis, Mr Palmer—they all use it—and now you sir. There won't be much room to swing a cat."

John liked Kilroy, but decided he needed putting down. "If you're working here, Mr Kilroy, you're working for me. I hope we'll get on."

He extended his hand and Kilroy grasped it firmly, aware that he was clinching some sort of deal and not in the least deflated. "I hope you'll be happy here, sir. They're a nice bunch."

The door closed and John heard the retreating footsteps and the clank of the lift gate—alone in his cell—monastic or prison, he wasn't sure. He put his hat and umbrella on the window sill, and looked out at the roofs of the other buildings. There was a skyline, but not enough of it to gaze upon. He crossed to another door and opened it—a broom cupboard? No—a small unoccupied room with a window—the sun just creeping in. He stepped round the bucket and mop. The skyline was quite visible—St. Paul's Cathedral among it . . . That's better. This would be the General Manager's office.

He returned to the main room and unearthed the telephone. He imagined this was how the lower end of Fleet Street looked the morning after.

"Hullo."

A slightly doubtful voice answered.

"Mr Burrows, sir?"

"Mr Burrows isn't here yet. I'm the General Manager—who are you?"

"Doreen Bottle."

"Well, Miss Bottle, if anybody rings up and asks for the B.B.C., put him through to me."

"Yes, sir."

"And meanwhile put me through to Dunblane 536."

"You'll have to hold on."

"Ring me back. I'm busy."

Miss Bottle gave an interrupted gulp and he put the receiver down, conscious that she would now be anxiously and speedily connecting him to his home. Muriel would be at breakfast, probably reading the postcard he'd sent her. He made a mental note of his new number to give her . . .. The clank of the distant lift heralded the arrival of the others, and he took up a position with his back to the window.

Burrows was the first to enter the office, followed by Lewis. They were laughing together, apparently not the least concerned that they were about to meet their new boss for the first time.

"Hullo," said Burrows. "You must be. . ."

"John Reith—Mr Burrows, I presume."

Burrows smiled cheerfully and introduced Lewis. He was not the least intimidated by the giant Scot silhouetted in the window—after all, the General Manager was very much the new boy and would be far too busy organising the company to find time to do much about the programmes.

He was left in peace for exactly three days—that was how long it took John to read every book on broadcasting that he could lay his hands on, and to absorb the business side of his new appointment. He approached the sheer slog of acquiring information like the highly trained engineer that he was. Read all you can on the subject, then go down on the floor and gain experience. He'd spent the first five years of his working life getting up at five and going to bed at ten—during his first week at the B.B.C. he had four hours sleep a night. He didn't mind going without sleep—in fact in later years, if he couldn't sleep, he'd leave the house at 3 a.m., go to his office and then return home for breakfast at eight. Then he would go back to his office to start the day along with everyone else, having already done a day's work.

He opened his office door.

"Mr Burrows, I should like to draw on your experience. Would you like to show me round the Studio?"

Burrows was making up the office betting list prior to arranging the programmes for the day.

"I'm going down there now—do you want to come?"

"Yes, if you don't mind."

"I'll be with you in half a minute."

"I thought you said 'now'."

John took his hat from the newly installed stand and stood by the door. Burrows got up, deciding to forget the horses for the moment.

John said: "You've forgotten your list. Put a pound on each way for me."

"What do you fancy?"

"I leave that to you. You're the expert." There was nothing ironic in the remark—Burrows felt he'd been given a command.

Two days later, John filled in his diary. It had been an exciting and stimulating week. In addition to meeting the Board he visited the studio and made the acquaintance of Rex Palmer, who not only ran the London Station but also provided the entertainment at times—singing *"Abide with me"* to close the day at 9 o'clock. Reith took to him and Lewis immediately. Lewis was in sharp contrast to Burrows who worried greatly if a Norfolk vicar wrote in to say he'd detected someone using a swear word. Lewis didn't give a damn and said so. John liked the way in which the problems of providing two hours of programmes was handled with such zeal and ingenuity, but he was sadly disappointed by the general makeshift attitude of the technical side.

The sudden departure of the head of engineering was the natural corollary of John's almost biblical philosophy. He was much too sensible to open his Bible at any old place and shut his eyes and plonk one finger down to give himself a text. He simply paused momentarily with his pen aloft and waited till the door was shut on the back of the engineer rat. It occurred to him at once—"He who is not for me is against me." So perish all traitors. And he set about getting a replacement.

The more he thought about it, the better he was pleased with his precipitate action. Whereas the Board had little interest in anything but the active business of making a programme which would sell their wirelesses to the largest number of people, John was concerned to create an organisation capable of broadcasting programmes of quality. He realised that the B.B.C. was no better than any of the other companies. In fact they lagged behind in many respects. One of their problems was that of interference from other stations broadcasting on the same wavelengths. In particular there was one called The Writtle, operating from Clemsford. The success with which they managed to make their voice heard during the B.B.C.'s children's programme was the object of amusement to listeners and of profound irritation to

1.   *Reith's mother*

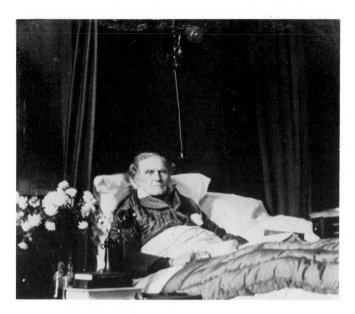

2. *Reith's father in bed*

3. *Charlie Bowser and Muriel in uniform*

4. *Tom Fleming as Reith in the B.B.C. dramatisation. Flanders 1915: "Blood everywhere. My new uniform is ruined." (B.B.C. Enterprises)*

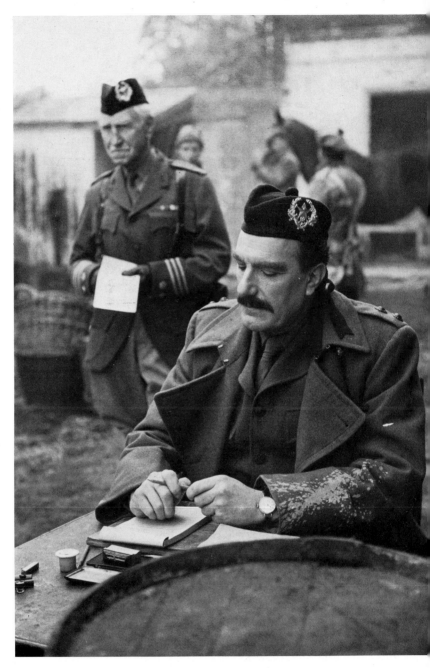

5.   *Tom Fleming portrays Reith as a Transport Officer in 1914 in the B.B.C. dramatisation: "It was expedient to be on friendly terms with me. I was a power in the land." (B.B.C. Enterprises)*

Burrows and the others. "Hullo Tock Emma, hullo Tock Emma,
this is 'Writtle' calling. We will now play you a record of Dame
Clara Butt singing *Land of Hope and Glory*, but first I'd like to tell
you what I had for lunch . . ." And the voice would go on
cracking jokes and reciting revamped nursery rhymes till the
B.B.C.'s item was almost obliterated. John's reaction was to ask
Burrows who the culprit was and invite him to call.

Burrows rang up the Writtle and spoke to Peter Eckersley. He
advised him to apply at once for the job left vacant by the
engineer, and he told the General Manager that the reason that
the Writtle continually lampooned the B.B.C. was because
Eckersley was bored by sitting round a table in a wooden hut.
He was in fact a brilliant wireless engineer who had served with
distinction in the R.F.C. and was longing to break the bonds
which were keeping broadcasting in the Stone Age. "He's a radio
genius," was Burrows, summing up.

It didn't take John five minutes of conversation in his cramped
office to know that Peter Eckersley was the man he was after.
Burrows was afraid that the dour Scot would not take kindly to
the ribald humour and Air Force slang which flowed endlessly
from the "radio genius". But John was looking deeper than the
outward and visible: like a prophet with a new disciple, he was
seeking the man beneath. He wanted someone with a vision of
broadcasting to complement his own, a vision soundly based on
scientific knowledge—capable of planning new radio stations
and equipment, but all the time with a vision of the wireless
waves connecting one town with another, one country with
another. . .

"Are you a Christian?" he asked.

"C. of E.," replied Eckersley with a smile. "That covers most
things."

He waited for the expected smile in return. It didn't come.
There was a sternness and gauntness about Mr Reith which
made him feel he was in the presence of his old headmaster, or
at any rate someone several years his senior instead of almost
the same age. He waited for the next question—his Air Force
career perhaps, which school or university . . . ?

John looked steadily into the other man's eyes. They were

somewhat thyroid, he decided, but otherwise . . .

"Are you married?"

"Oh yes. Are you?"

"Oh yes indeed. She's up in Scotland, would you like to see round the Studio?"

"Very much."

John got up and pointed to a certificate hanging on the wall behind his desk. "You see that?"

It looked like a certificate for regular attendance at Sunday School.

"Come and look. See the signature. Should appeal to you."

Peter was able to decypher it.

"Clerk Maxwell?" he asked in surprise.

"He taught my father Natural Philosophy in the early days. It was one of his most treasured possessions and now it's mine. I find it significant that the Scotsman who discovered wireless should have taught my father and that I should be, in a sense, his pupil too. My father was not a scientist—he was a man of God."

The General Manager's father stared stiffly at Peter from the window sill. John continued: "I shall value your opinion, even if you don't accept the job."

Job? What job? Had he been offered the job?

The Studio was only a short distance down the Strand, but John strode out as though on a ten-mile hike. They arrived as the evening programme neared its end: John was conscious that Peter was largely joining the B.B.C because the Writtle was such an amateur outfit. He glanced round at their own studio. This boasted a green curtain to muffle the echo, a microphone tied up with string, and the circuit completed by dropping a sixpence into the contacts—hardly the professional broadcasting system of the future.

The programme ended at nine with Aunt Sophie demurely playing the piano and Rex Palmer singing a hymn—not *Abide with me* on this occasion.

At their first meeting, John had chilled the normally warm atmosphere by stating his views plainly to Palmer—"I like your voice, but you're not paid to sing. You're paid to run the London

Broadcasting Station, and I don't think much of it. This Studio's hopelessly ill-equipped what's more. But don't be disheartened, that's easily put right, and—as we say in Glasgow—that's a fact." Now "the fact" was gazing with an interested smile at the conglomeration of equipment behind the green curtain.

"Captain Eckersley, I want to introduce you to the rest of the team."

So he'd got the job? Or had he?

Burrows he knew of old. "Hullo C.Q., Tock Emma Writtle," the Programme Controller welcomed him. "You can't beat us so you'd better join us."

He shook hands all round.

"Shall we go to a public house" asked John unexpectedly. "There's probably one in the vicinity."

Lewis appeared shocked. "Our General Manager's been here three weeks and he's never been to the 'Coal Hole'!"

Over a half-consumed pint of bitter, John challenged Peter to create the technical side of the British Broadcasting Company. "What microphone do you use at the Writtle?"

"One I designed myself."

"Good, because the equipment we shall require hasn't even been thought of yet. I'm not talking abour interior pediments, I'm talking about transmitters. We've got to put up eight of them immediately—it's a condition of the licence."

He could see that Peter was impressed.

"Cardiff, Birmingham and Glasgow to start with. And I'm not talking about a factory chimney with an aerial stuck on the top— it's a tremendous undertaking. Do you think you can do it?"

Ah!—So this was the offer. "Yes, I can do it."

"In that case the job's yours." John held out his hand over the beer tankard.

Peter had two more pints, but John only sipped from his. He was teetotal, but in view of the importance of the occasion he felt justified in modifying his stance.

"I shall need my own office, and the technical staff will be Marconi's I suppose?"

John frowned. "Marconi's? No, no."

"Why—aren't they any good? Peter was surprised at John's vehemence.

"They're excellent—but they're not ours. From now on every-thing must belong to the B.B.C."

Peter looked round at the others as Lewis brought him another pint. "I see. What am I to be called? Director of Engineering?"

"Chief Engineer—will that do you?"

Burrows smiled. "Our first and only—and therefore our Chief."

"Q.E.D.," added John amid laughter. "I must remind you, though, that I'm a fully qualified engineer myself." More laughter.

But Peter didn't join in. "You see," he said, "If I take this on, I want to be in charge—sole charge." If? Was he turning the job down—the job of a lifetime—the job of his dreams. It had to be said, and he repeated it. "Sole charge."

There was a fractional hesitation while John drained the last inch of his tankard. It was a dramatic pause. John had a sense of timing which might have made six-foot-six of theatrical history. "I expect everyone who works for me to do his job his own way to the best of his ability. I'll back you to the hilt, Captain Eckersley, but if you put a foot wrong, you'll have to account to me—Chief Engineer or no Chief Engineer."

"Q.E.D.," said Peter.

13

Muriel was pleased with the furnished flat in Queen Anne's Mansions, but disappointed that she had had no hand in its choice. John pointed out that he couldn't very well refuse to take advantage of the kindness of the member of the Board to whom the flat belonged, and that they'd be lucky to find anything nearly as nice or convenient if they searched around for a year.

"Convenient for what?" asked Muriel.

"It's a stone's throw from the House of Commons and not far from where I plan to have the new studios in the Strand. Regent's Square is good for the dog and I've been in the church and they've got just the sort of service Mother likes with very good music."

"Convenient for you."

Muriel had made her small protest the same as usual. Although she was so shy and reserved—he habitually kept telling her so at any rate—she had a firm notion as to her rights. John had one equally firm conviction—the conviction that where decisions of any importance were concerned, he was the one to make them. Muriel could protest . . . afterwards.

Next Sunday they went to church. Twice. "I didn't much like the service," she commented, unasked.

"Then try your luck with St. Margaret's or Westminster Abbey. What have you got against religion?"

"I don't much enjoy going to church, John."

He said nothing more, but a few weeks later they were returning from a stroll in St. James's Park. John was thinking of his mother, and wondering how she would enjoy her first visit to their new home. She was coming down on the overnight from

Dumfries. As they turned a corner, he stopped and jabbed his
umbrella at a crack in the paving stones—another thing to
complain to the council about—he'd already got them to move a
street lamp.

"Musie," he said patiently, "there is nothing finer than the
King James' Bible, the English Prayer Book and the Scottish
hymns which illuminate the psalms of David."

"All the same . . ." Her second small protest was over.

They mounted the front steps and entered their new home.
Two suitcases were blocking the study door. Muriel saw them at
the same moment—she'd seen them both before, and dreaded
their appearance: one scratched and battered heavy leather, the
other a modern revelation, bulging under a strap. They were like
their owners. Mother and Jean had arrived from Scotland.

The subject of Jean's impending divorce was bound to come
up at any moment—the visit with Mother was only part natural
curiosity. Muriel had watched John avoiding all mention of
Graham throughout supper. He was against Jean. As he'd said to
Muriel, "Jean made her vow—whom God has joined together,
let no man put asunder." Useless for Muriel to point out that the
marriage had not been consummated and therefore God didn't
come into it. If she was on anyone's side she was on Jean's. Why
should she be expected to spend the rest of her days in India or
wherever Graham decided to go? As for Mother, she tried to
comfort and advise with the faint hope that God would intervene
and make everything right. She was thankful that George had
not lived to see this day.

"Nearly seven—let's hear the News Bulletin." John got up
abruptly, disentangling Muriel's knitting from his shoe.

"Oh, we're going to hear the wireless at last"—there was more
than a hint of bitchery in Jean's voice.

John switched on the wireless and waited for it to warm up.

"We've not had it long. It's the very latest model," explained
Muriel. She raised her voice for Mother's benefit. "John's given
one to the Archbishop of Canterbury."

"The Archbishop of Canterbury!" Mother was terribly impressed.

"When I showed him ours he though we ought to keep the

window open to improve the reception." A high-pitched whistle.
"It's coming through."

"What's he doing? What's wrong with it?" asked Jean with
distaste.

"He's tuning it."

"Like a piano?"

"You have to find the wavelength."

"Wavelength, what's that?"

"Well it's . . . " Muriel was almost as vague as Jean in her
knowledge of the new miracle.

"Shush, Jean, Shush!" John bent over the back of the wireless
and tried the aerial in another hole.

The voice of Burrows came up quite clearly. "This is London
calling on all stations. Here is the News at 7 o'clock."

He switched it off again. "There, what did you think of that
Muriel?"

"Think of what?"

"We've changed the call signal. From now on it's just 'London
calling'. What do you think of that?"

"Oh, much better."

"Say if you preferred 'This is 2LO calling on all stations'."

Muriel smiled. "No, no, 'London calling' sounds far better,
doesn't it, Jean?"

"Don't ask me. I haven't got a wireless set. I can't afford one."

John was quick to detect the acid reproach. "Is that a hint or an
accusation?" he asked.

"Both. You're supposed to be manager of the B.B.C., and . . ."

"Not supposed—I am!"

"Yet your own sister hasn't even got a wireless set."

"You think I should give one to all my relatives?"

"Why not? You gave one to the Archbishop of Canterbury."

John boiled inwardly. How dare she make major acts of
policy into a family bicker? She might as well complain that he'd
given one to the King. . .

Jean was going on. "Personally I think the wireless is nothing
but a waste of time."

That was too much. "Jean, you can pack your bags and go!"

"Where? I haven't any money—I haven't any home . . ."

"You have a perfectly good husband—go back to him."

"He's a perfectly horrible husband."

"John dear, for my sake, please," his mother could see that Jean was near to tears.

"All right, for your sake, Mother." He sat down heavily and picked up the paper. "Oh, I daresay it's easy enough to break your marriage vows when you can live with your mother while I foot the bill."

"Has it never occurred to you that Mother's an old lady who would rather live with her daughter than live alone?"

"Seventy-five, I don't call that old."

"John please . . ." Muriel put a soothing hand on his and he fumed in silence.

For Jean it was a small skirmish won in their ceaseless battle. She reached for her book. "Shall I read to you, Mother?"

John pounced before her. "I'll do that. Don't pretend you look after her, she looks after herself!"

"Jean's company for me," pleaded Mrs Reith.

"That sort of company you can very well do without."

"I'm her daughter."

"More's the pity. He thumbed through the book. *Bulldog Drummond.* She doesn't want that!"

"You're only jealous," Jean persisted.

"She likes biography—Jealous!"

"If you know a better word. . . "

"I'm not more jealous of you than I am of the cat! Sits all day long in front of the fire and demands the top of the milk. If you want a word for what I am as regards you, it's 'Ashamed'!" He got up and flung the book down on the piano.

"Never mind, Jean," said Muriel. This was only the first day of the visit and they were here for a fortnight.

Jean was almost in tears, "I'm sorry, Muriel, but why does he invite me down here when all he wants to do is quarrel?"

"I didn't invite you—I invited Mother!"

"You sent me a rail ticket."

"Yes, First Class—a return. So why don't you use it?"

"John how can you . . .?" Jean was finally reduced and the tears gushed like a sudden fountain. "I'm your sister. What do you want?"

And she hurried out.

Muriel folded her knitting away. "Oh, John dear, you've spoiled the evening." She got up.

"She's spoiled it! Don't go after her—that's all she wants—to upset everybody!"

John was right. But Jean was Muriel's sister-in-law, and the years stretched ahead . . . were they to be years of endless family rows? She went off to the kitchen and made a pot of tea and put it on a tray with a bowl of sugar and a jug of milk and took it up to Jean in her bedroom.

As she passed the drawing room door she could see John sitting peacefully with his mother. John turned his head.

"Mind the milk doesn't go sour," he called. His mother sighed. "I'm sorry Mother."

His mother sighed again. "You don't need to say sorry to me."

"Well I'm not saying it to Jean." He looked away from her, and then turned back. Seventy-five! She didn't look more than sixty. He wanted her happiness more than anything. "Shall we say a prayer together? A broken and contrite heart?" He came over to her and knelt beside her. How many times had they knelt together? In church? The nursery—beside his bed before she kissed him goodnight. At such times his restless, irrepressible nature found peace. . .

14

Lord Gainford, Chairman of the Board, was doubtful how his vigorous and independent General Manager would receive the news that they wanted to appoint a Deputy to help him run the now burgeoning enterprise. They'd hit on a recently retired naval officer, Vice Admiral Charles Carpendale, as the man for the job. So he invited John and Muriel to dinner at his home and during the course of the evening raised the subject. He was surprised to find that, far from resenting an intrusion into what had hitherto been entirely his preserve, John welcomed the idea of delegating some of the responsibilities.

"If you hadn't said it, I'd have brought the matter up at our next meeting."

Gainford didn't appreciate that John planned to raise another matter himself. The office and studio accommodation at Magnet House was now quite inadequate, and he'd only that morning had a look round empty premises at Savoy Hill, just off the Strand near the Savoy Hotel. The building was far too large for their present needs, but at the rate they were expanding if would be fully occupied in five years and bursting at the seams in ten. Now that Gainford had got his way over Carpendale, John felt he could hardly object to new and larger premises. He also calculated that if he could get Carpendale to agree with him, the rest of the Board would have to do the same. He made a few enquiries of Miss Shields, his newly appointed Secretary. She had formerly worked for Lloyd George. There was no one of importance that she didn't know. "Admiral Carpendale? Oh, he's delightful!" she'd told him. "Very navy, of course, free and easy, bright and breezy."

John rang him up. He wanted his deputy to start as he meant to go on—as a friend. He needn't have worried. They got on from the word go.

John found himself talking, not only about the B.B.C. as it was at that moment, but as he saw it in the future. Selling wireless sets was all very well for a business man, and no doubt he could devote his life to such an enterprise if he wanted—but for John there had to be something more. He had gone on for the last few months, increasingly aware that he needed more than an expansion programme to fuel his enthusiasm. The fact that Charlie had turned down the job made him question the whole of his commitment to broadcasting, and search for a higher ideal—a mast to nail his flag to. Having found it, he determined to confront the Board. He'd more than fulfilled his part of the bargain—sales had doubled, the B.B.C. dominated the market place—now the Board must make a declaration of faith. When he interviewed anyone for the job, he always asked, "Are you a Christian?" and if not "What are you?". The coward, the shirker, the brainless and inept, the disloyal and defunct were revealed immediately. To be any good to John a man had to have convictions above and beyond mere training and expertise.

The Board, however had no notion what was in store for them when they met as usual on that Friday in April.

John's new office at Savoy Hill had a splendid view up and down the Thames—St. Paul's to the East and Westminster to the right. He also liked the gable ends which flanked the window, and gave a perspective to it all. He could no longer chase a record to the top of the Cairngorms, but he frequently used the stairs, arriving breathless at the top. Another advantage was that a run up the staircase encompassed the whole building—offices and studios—and gave him the sense of being part of the organisation, and not merely a cherry on top of the cake—or better perhaps, the eagle in his eyrie.

Apart from Peter having made the new studios the best in the country, there were decent facilities for people who were expected to work all hours. John had found an old notice which read, "Knock and Wait." He'd turned it over and it now hung on the front door—"B.B.C. Walk in!" As a son of the manse, he was accustomed to the front door being permanently open to callers, and as General Manager he needed to know that there was nobody and nothing between him and whoever wished to see him—distinguished visitor or head of a department, or charlady worried about her rent. Weekly meetings of departmental heads became known as "Controller's Meetings", and they were conducted informally in the Board Room. This room was yet another manifestation of John's total inability to separate his office from his home. Other managers had offices and Board Rooms of Dickensian gloom. But the visitor to John Reith might find himself in the Board Room and think he'd strayed into a drawing room. Pleasantly furnished and decorated, it was calculated to relax even the most nervous newcomer to broad-casting. And when it came to Board Meetings, it was difficult for the Chairman to get in a lather across a large vase of whatever flowers John had bought off the barrow at Charing Cross.

Lord Gainford had made his money out of coal. But he had imagination—not too much or he might have foreseen the Leviathan he was nursing in what was only a subsidiary company. He and the other members of the Board always enjoyed their meetings enormously. John gave them a meticu-lous report upon every aspect of the business, and then they all adjourned to the Drawing Room for a full Scottish High Tea. Often they were joined by members of the staff who were implicated in an aspect of the prior discussions. The Smokies and kippers were beautifully fresh. "Direct from Stonehaven where I was born—so you might call them the fruits of my Baptism."

Mr Pease, who was from North America and prided himself in forceful thinking—it was he who had suggested changing the laborious call sign "2LO calling on all stations" to "London calling"—was a little late. He came in with Burrows and Peter Eckersley, having made a tour of inspection. He interrupted the conversation. "Savoy Hill's rather large—don't you think we should share these premises, John?"

"Certainly not," John quickly scotched the idea. "We've got to have room for expansion. Apart from anything else I've got to have room to stretch my legs." The knock-out punch followed by a warm sponge.

Pease was not to be put off. "By expansion, do you mean an increase in the actual time broadcast or what?"

"You'd better answer that, Burrows."

"I asked you, John."

"Burrows is in charge of programmes, sir, not me." He shifted the ground to the formal. It brought the other members of the Board into the conversation, and they were delighted with Savoy Hill.

Burrows stepped forward eagerly. "We'll have more time, and therefore more programmes—music, drama, talks and religion."

"Religion?" Even Gainford looked uneasy.

"We're introducing a Sunday morning service."

"With the blessing of the Archbishop of Canterbury, of course," John added, as though assuming that their religious susceptibilities were being infringed.

"Religious services will hardly increase our business." Pease again. "We mustn't forget we're a private company, and the only reason we're here today is to sell wirelesses. More and more wirelesses."

Carpendale saw John look away to hide a frown. "Don't worry Mr Pease." He proffered a scone. "The business side of the enterprise is always well to the fore in my mind, I promise you. And the proof of the pudding is that your sales have more than doubled in the last six months."

Pease accepted the scone. "Yes, well . . . I just thought I'd mention it."

"We're all very grateful, I'm sure," said Gainford weakly.

"You've no need to be, sir," said John, coming back into the conversation. "I can say this for all of us—it's a great joy and a privilege to work with such a pleasant and helpful Board of directors."

Peter and Burrows said, "Hear, hear" loudly, knowing from experience that John was about to play a trump. "There's just one thing—while we're on the subject, as it were."

Gainford was looking at his watch, thinking about meeting his wife at the Savoy—so conveniently round the corner.

John savoured the uneasy silence. "I assume this Board is totally committed to broadcasting."

Gainford looked round. His Board appeared as nonplussed as he was. It was as though a colliery manager had asked him if he were totally committed to coal.

John went on. "I myself am totally committed to broadcasting as such. To that end I will exert myself to the utmost. The same goes for the rest of us—Burrows, Eckersley, Lewis. We don't mind how long we work, or how or when. What about the Board?"

"We'll back you, of course," said Gainford lamely.

"But this dedication could mean a divergence of interest on a matter of principle."

Mr Pease thought he could deal with the situation. "I take it we're talking about *financial* commitment, Mr Reith?"

"No sir—principle."

"That's rather vague."

"No sir—in my case a principle is most specific."

"Well in my opinion, Mr Reith, your principles are your own concern." Lord Gainford wasn't going to be drawn into some sort of religious discussion. "As long as you give us a full report every month so that we can know how you're getting on—we're satisfied."

The rest of the Board nodded compliantly.

"Does that answer your question?"

"I didn't ask a question sir—I made a statement."

"You're a difficult man to argue with." Gainford was dimly aware that for John some personal conflict was being resolved—but it had gone six, and his wife would be waiting. "Let's say we trust you to do your best, and that's good enough for us. Is that good enough for you?"

"I couldn't ask for more." John grasped Gainford's hand warmly.

"My wife's over at the Savoy, would you like to join us?" invited Gainford to cover his embarrassment. It was obvious to him that their General Manager was an exceptional individual, doing an exceptional job for the company, but he sometimes wished he didn't seek to elevate ordinary business into the higher realms of ethics and . . . well, principles.

"I'm afraid I've got Marconi and Sir Oliver Lodge in the studio this evening. Why don't you and your wife join us after the broadcast?"

"Yes, yes, indeed. Thank you so much—thank you". He hurried off to tell his wife, who would now forgive him for keeping her waiting, and the rest of the Board departed in their usual good spirits.

Peter remained behind to ask John's opinion about his scheme to rationalise the European networks. John gave him the go-ahead—as usual. "I think we're very lucky, Peter. We've got a first-rate Board."

"You mean you've got a Board that lets you do what you like."

"They let me do what's right—that's the important thing."

Peter smiled—unable to compete with John's irrepressible conviction that he had a mission in life. "Oh, by the way, do you think my brother Roger could come and see you?" he asked.

"Yes, of course. What for?"

"He's looking for a job. He's not a bad chap. He can get on with anyone."

"I rather mistrust people of that ilk," said John with his usual directness. "But send him along. I daresay I can find him something to tide him over—for your sake, if for no other reason."

He meant it. Peter was his right hand, pushing the frontiers of broadcasting across the globe, cheerful and friendly and open. In many ways Peter was the complete opposite to himself—no questions to be answered, no inner conflicts . . . other than matrimonial. Perhaps he could be of help. Muriel was a great peacemaker. "I tell you what—you and Stella come to supper on Thursday and bring Roger with you."

Peter hesitated. "Yes, thank you John. I'll have to ask Stella, but I expect she'll want to come."

"Good."

Peter left, and John heard him whistling as he went towards the lift. Peter was such a nice man. Why he had to get hitched to a woman like Stella . . . ? She reminded him of Maisie—Jezebel and Charlie. . . What happened to him since he got married?

Why had he become so weak and vascillating like Ahab? No, no, that wasn't true. Charlie was his best friend, and would remain so. He wasn't going to give him up to that wretched woman.

Such thoughts were momentary. He went up to his office to prepare an official welcome for the two great pioneers of wireless. It was a good omen surely, that such a visit should mark the day on which John Walsham Reith decided to remove broadcasting from the clutches of the business fraternity, and place it where it belonged—on the altar of God.

Reith at his desk

From the B.B.C. dramatisation. Prime Minister Baldwin (Peter Barkworth) gets ready to speak to the nation as Reith looks over his speech: "Suddenly I had qualms about the word 'dignity' that I'd written into his speech." (B.B.C. Enterprises)

8.   *Tom Fleming as Reith in the B.B.C. dramatisation: "This day—May 2nd, 1932—belongs to you all." (B.B.C. Enterprises)*

Reith (Tom Fleming) on his knees at his scrapbook, helped out by his secretary, Miss Stanley (Julia Hills)—from the B.B.C dramatisation. (B.B.C. Enterprises)

Filming REITH at Aldershot for the B.B.C. dramatisation. The author, Roger Milner (centre) with Tom Fleming on his right and producer, Innes Lloyd, on his left. (B.B.C. Enterprises)

11.   *Reith and Ramsay Macdonald*

15

In 1924 they moved house from Scotland. All their favourite bits and pieces came with them, and looked one hundred per cent better for their change of scenery. Number 6, Barton Street, was an ideal choice. Muriel liked it because it was quite small and cosy—rather like her uncle's town house. Uncle William liked it too. He could just manage the steps, being crippled with arthritis. John preferred him to most of Muriel's relatives, and admired his dogged spirit in fighting his disease, and his unswerving determination to get compensation for a bomb that had dropped on his printing works during the war. "Six years, and still not a penny. But I'll get it or die in the attempt."

The Odhams as a bunch were kept at arm's length. Partly because they belonged to the "self-made man class" but mostly because Odhams Press gave them considerable power and influence. John had firmly set his face against anything which might reflect on his unbiased integrity.

Early in the year, Gainford had suggested that John write a book about broadcasting. He set to work with a will and produced a manuscript within a few weeks. "There you are," he said, laying it before Muriel as though she'd asked him to do it. "What do you think of that?"

"Oh, I think it's marvellous. Are you going to get Uncle William to publish it?"

"Certainly not. Nor will he ever publish any magazine or anything else connected with the B.B.C.." He was thinking of the *Radio Times* which Uncle William had originally volunteered to print. "I'm not Director of a family business," he said scornfully.

Muriel didn't go on about it now. She'd only get hurt. After all,

she had shares in the family business, John always took a lively
interest in the fluctuations of Odhams on the Stock Market. But
of course he couldn't be a shareholder. The integrity of his
beloved B.B.C.! Sometimes Muriel felt almost rebellious.

With the move to Barton Street, the honeymoon was over. No
longer were they newly weds up from Scotland. John was a man
with a position in society, and his wife had to take her rightful
place beside him. He enjoyed the experience. She didn't.

Socialising among the great and powerful did not come easily
to Muriel. The more she tried, the harder it seemed to become
for her. John put it down to her upbringing. He'd always
lectured her about being dominated by her parents, urging her
to break free. It was like putting sugar on porridge—"Try it with
salt, Musie—just try it!

"I have tried it, John, and I don't like it."

"Because your mother and father didn't like porridge, so you
don't like it!"

It was useless for her to argue. Useless to try and explain that
she was naturally reserved and shy and always would be, and
that thrusting her forward into political society made matters
worse. John saw that he was making no progress with her, and
determined to improve himself by taking lessons in psychiatry.
Of course he told her it was in order to understand the workings
of the female mind! He was confident that he would easily have
set up in business, but he had to admit that his efforts to pass on
his knowledge to Muriel had only been moderately successful.
She was a competent housekeeper, but no more. He also felt that
his brother's deteriorating health might be better understood. On
the last occasion that he'd been able to see Douglas, they'd gone
out together for tea. The conversation was perfectly sensible, but
Douglas had developed an inane laugh with which he punctuated every remark. John found it hard not to show irritation,
though he knew it was not Douglas's fault in any way. It was a
disease, perhaps incurable. John sympathised deeply with him
and prayed for him, and supported him financially, but he did
not understand him any more than he understood his sister
Jean—and no amount of psychiatric evening classes could prevent him from disliking her intensely. Yes—his own sister and

he really couldn't stand the sight of her. Partly, he didn't disguise
the truth from himself, it was because of her attitude to her
divorce proceedings. She was so intent on securing a settlement
in her favour that she never for one moment seemed to care
about the damage she might do to others. He'd told her at their
last meeting.

"If you don't love him, leave him alone."

"I don't see why he should be allowed to get away with it."

"You don't have to take it to the House of Lords!"

"Why shouldn't I?"

"Because . . . because you're making a fool of yourself."

"Because I'm your sister, and it might make a fool of you!" she
retorted hotly.

"I just feel damned sorry for Graham! You're a vindictive and
spiteful woman, with nothing better to do than drag the poor
fellow through the mire."

"And you are arrogant and selfish and don't think anybody is
worth thinking about but yourself."

"Untrue. Totally untrue."

"You're spoilt! You always were, and you still are—spoilt,
spoilt, spoilt!" She nearly pulled his hair as she used to do in the
nursery.

When she'd gone back to Scotland, having had her appeal
dismissed by the Lords, he had one of his usual attacks of
remorse and remembered her at Christmas with a generous
cheque. She was perfectly right to castigate him. She had put her
finger on a sore spot when she accused him of selfishness.
Nevertheless, he was the Manager of the B.B.C., recently
promoted, and at a time when Caesar was mounting the steps. of
the Forum, it would have helped if Caesar's sister had been
reasonably above reproach!

John, being a Scot, saw no need to make a fuss of the
Christmas festival beyond taking his mother to the church in St.
Stephen's Square to try out some new hearing aid equipment. It
had been installed at his suggestion. Mrs Reith didn't like it and
said so. John was irritated by her seeming lack of interest. He
loved his mother dearly, and looked forward to her visits. Yet
almost inevitably there were arguments and tears. It was as

though by making her suffer, he could endure the pangs of remorse and doubt without which he couldn't enjoy the forgiveness and thanksgiving. According to his psychiatric lessons he suffered from a "guilt complex"—or rather "enjoyed a guilt complex". So he took advantage of the rancorous atmosphere after lunch to retire to his study, and smoke contentedly while he wrote up his diary. Muriel heaved a sigh of relief. Only one more week and the dreaded visit would be over. If she'd kept a diary it would have been one long list of things that had to be done before, during and after. Before was the worst. John became increasingly critical of everything she did. Even the flowers in his mother's bedroom had to be replaced five minutes before her arrival. Muriel's every movement was scrutinised to make sure it would not upset Mother if she were there. If she slipped on the polished floor it would make John rise in horror. "Suppose that had happened to Mother! From now on no floors are to be polished till January 2nd." Same with the central heating—it was too hot or too cold—and the light by her bed was too near or too far . . . As though Muriel was deliberately setting traps for her mother-in-law like a mole! Muriel resented all this, but understood the cause better than John did. She loved John and realised that his faults were not intentional, and that the moment his mother had gone he'd put his arms round her and give her a kiss and then they'd go for a walk in St. James's Park and talk to the ducks. He wasn't like Muriel, able to relax and do nothing. Even a walk in the park had to involve time and distance and keeping fit . . . and feeding the ducks.

Mother went up to rest, Muriel read a biography of General Roberts that John had given her—he'd be asking her what she thought over supper—and John read what he'd just written.

John had finally moulded the B.B.C. into something worthy to be offered up. There had been dangers that the Government would allow foreign radio sets to swamp the market and thus destroy the whole business security of the company; there had been newspaper owners and theatre managers, and politicians—all fearful that this new fangled instrument would somehow ruin them. John had faced committees of enquiry and Press Barons

and warlords without yielding a single principle. How many
hours had he spent at how many dinners? How many sessions at
the House of Commons? How many cigars had he smoked at the
Athenaeum? But at the end of it all, he still wasn't sure that he'd
be granted the Charter he sought—"Monopoly under God" he'd
called it.

1926 would settle his hash one way or the other. But like a
prisoner conducting his own defence, he had caught the
imagination of the public, and the eye of the judge. When
Baldwin became Prime Minister, he owed some part of his
success to the way in which he had been schooled in broadcasting technique by the young man from the B.B.C. John, being
meticulously fair, had also attempted to help the outgoing Prime
Minister, but Ramsay MacDonald thought he knew best. John
had told Peter "He wants us to broadcast his public speech
from Glasgow! The man's a fool." He had lost the election and a
few weeks later John had gone to see Baldwin.

The Prime Minister, having read the morning papers, had a
shrewd idea what was the purpose of the visit. The bully boys of
Fleet Street were softening up public opinion against the B.B.C.
The *Daily Express* led the field. "In a time of rising unemployment, the B.B.C. represents a challenge Fleet Street can no longer
ignore. Unless the Government acts soon, the newspapers will
be driven out of business. The B.B.C. in the pious words of son
of the Manse Reith, is taking the bread out of the mouths of
honest working men," Baldwin quoted the last sentence at John.

"Och well," said John, "Beaverbrook's a son of the Manse

"Though not so pious."

"Politics and power, that's all he's interested in."

"And you're not interested in power, Mr Reith?"

"I'm interested in the future of broadcasting in this country,
sir. Is the B.B.C. to be free and independent financially, or are we
to be the lackey of Fleet Street and Downing Street?"

"Do you prefer to be the lackey of big business?"

"No, Prime Minister, I do not! That's why I'm here."

Baldwin meditated. John didn't interrupt. Finally he gave a tug
at his waistcoat as though by doing so he could reduce the size

of his "corporation" to which his wife frequently alluded in
public. "My wife complains that I've got a 'corporation'—too
many banquets. Hm." He drew on his pipe. "And so, Mr Reith,
you want 'monopoly under God' I think you're reported as
saying."

"I did say that—yes, sir. We've initiated a lot of good things in
every line—music, schools broadcasts, talks, religion, politics,
discussions, news, but we've only had negative, or at the best,
timid approval from authority. Without monopoly, the B.B.C. will
have to play for safety, 'be popular', suit its clients. I shall have
to study diplomacy, curry favour, subordinate myself, like a
politician, to the vote, and produce programmes 'to the
reasonable satisfaction of the Postmaster General forsooth!'
What's the good of that? We need a Charter like the Bank of
England or the Royal Society. A Charter." He stopped and
awaited Baldwin's reaction.

"Tell you what I'll do," he said. "I'll set up a Commission of
Enquiry—all-party. Will that do?"

"It will do very well Prime Minister." And he got up as though
terminating the interview.

"Good. If you like to furnish me with the suggested terms of
reference." He looked up at John. "Gainford warned me that you
were rather a mountain of a man. I suppose you think you can
see further ahead than the ordinary ruck of humanity."

John smiled for the first time. He smiled again as he read
Baldwin's remark recorded in his diary. Yes, he could see further
ahead than most men, that was one of his great gifts—it was also
the cross he had to bear.

He turned back the pages and read the account of how he'd
flirted with his tennis partner and Muriel had got all steamed up
and said he didn't love her. He smiled to himself. That was half
the fun of keeping a diary . . . What did he do about it? He
turned the page. Invited the girl to tea which made Muriel
crosser than ever. Oh well . . . He reread his diary for Christmas
and added a complete list of all the presents he'd received—in
case he forgot to thank someone properly. Only seven presents
and three of them from the office. So much for Jean and Douglas
and . . .

He stopped abruptly. He'd suddenly remembered New Year's Eve. He was going to have to start the Highland Dancing at the Staff Ball. And when it came to dancing, he hardly knew one foot from the other. He hurried through to see Musie. "Musie, who do you know teaches Scottish Dancing?"

"Nobody."

"There must be somebody. I'll ring up the Scottish Office."

"There won't be anybody there. And in any case . . ."

"Ramsay MacDonald then—he'll know."

"You can't ring up the Prime Minister . . ."

"He's not the Prime Minister . . . I know—Harry Lauder—he's bound to know someone." And he rushed back to his study, and a moment later Muriel could hear him laughing and talking and doing his Glaswegian accent.

The following evening she returned to find the carpet rolled back and John prancing about to the gramophone. His instructress was a young and pretty girl with a very short skirt and long willowy legs.

Muriel remembered the tennis partner and turned towards the kitchen. John called out, "Come on, Musie—you've got to learn too! Take your shoes off!"

Winnie helped her off with her coat.

"You too, Winnie! Come on we'll make a foursome!"

Muriel and Winnie were reluctantly dragged into the drawing room. John still held on to the dance instructress. "Muriel this is Rita Wilmer—she's a friend of Harry Lauder, and she's going to come here every evening."

Muriel had learned the eightsome reel long ago, and the steps soon came back to her. John was so enthusiastic, she began to enjoy herself as he linked his arm in hers and swept her round in a circle. Her pangs of jealousy subsided too. Rita Wilmer had spots under her make-up, and she knew John liked a "good skin" to go with the long legs.

As for John, he was only concerned to hold his arms correctly and keep in step. But that night as he lay beside Muriel he gave a sigh.

"What was that for?" asked Muriel, ever on the defensive.

"I was reflecting on my misspent youth," replied John. "I'm a

Scotsman, born and bred, yet it's taken me thirty eight years to dance an eightsome reel."

New Year's Eve, and John duly astonished everyone by dancing a reel to perfection. He'd pretended to need help and protested that he'd burst his braces—that at least was true—he did. But at ten minutes to midnight he called a halt, and Muriel and he led some of the special guests to join the select few in the studio. Mrs Reith, his mother, was already seated in the place of honour, as though the whole thing was being done for her. As far as John was concerned, it was. He kissed her reverently and made Muriel stand beside her, so that he could see them together from his position by the microphone.

The clock ticked round to midnight, and then he signalled for the music to stop. He waited for Peter to give him the green light. The tension and drama appealed to the actor in him—and the thought that for millions of people the voice of John Reith would signify the end of one year and the start of another made his voice husky, and the deliberate tones seemed to carry a sense of sadness as he read from his carefully prepared script.

"Now the old year is coming to a close. For some of us 1925 may have been a year of unhappiness and we're glad to see the back of it. For others it may have seemed the high tide of achievement and endeavour and reward. But sadness or joy— none of us knows what's in store for us next. But we live in hopes."

He gave a prearranged signal for the sound of bells in the distance—as though he'd opened a window onto the new year. His mother was watching him, pride visible in every line on her face . . .

"Let us welcome the New Year to the sound of bells . . . and the words of Alfred Lord Tennyson.

> *Ring out the old, ring in the new,*
> *Ring happy bells, across the snow.*
> *The year is going, let it go:*
> *Ring out the false, ring in the true.*
>
> *Ring out false pride in place and blood,*
> *The civic slander and the spite,*

Ring in the love of truth and right,
Ring in the common love of good.

Ring out old shapes of foul disease:
Ring out the narrowing lust of gold;
Ring out the thousand wars of old,
Ring in the thousand years of peace.

Ring out the darkness of the land:
Ring in the Christ that is to be."

Midnight chimed, John had made his declaration of hope to the millions of listeners, and 1926 had begun.

16

John was just going to bed when the doorbell rang. He answered the door in his braces. It was a letter from the Prime Minister. He went to the phone and rang the B.B.C. "Burrows, I've just had a message from the Prime Minister. I'll be at the studio in half an hour. Tell Peter that all stations are to be connected with London for an S.B."

"Is it about the strike?"

"Don't mention the word strike—just interrupt the programme now, and tell all stations to stand by for an important announcement at midnight."

He then rang the P.M.'s secretary Wilson to tell him he'd make the announcement himself and ran upstairs to Muriel.

"As I thought, they're going on strike."

"Who are?"

"The coal miners." No good explaining to Muriel the whys and wherefores—she neither knew nor cared. "I'm going over to the studio now—I'll be back as soon as possible. You get off to sleep."

"Of course I won't get off to sleep. I shall sit up and listen to the wireless."

He gave her a quick kiss. "I'll make the announcement. Lucky I'm still in my dinner jacket."

He hurried downstairs, two at a time. Muriel heard the front door bang and put on her dressing gown. She thought it rather funny that John should have to wear his dinner jacket in order to make his announcement—after all nobody could see him. He could be in his pyjamas

Burrows and Peter were both at the Savoy Hill, and there was a general air of excitement. John sat on a chair in the corner of the studio and reread the Prime Minister's message. He took out his pen. "I'll just put this into English." At midnight Muriel, like a million other anxious citizens, including the Prime Minister, heard the voice of John Reith, the voice of the British Broadcasting Company, announce that "all coal production has now ceased, and the public is advised to conserve supplies." The General Strike was about to begin.

The following day the Government continued to make last-ditch efforts to save the situation. John rang Uncle William and learned that the print unions would shut down every newspaper in the country. He put the phone down gleefully. "The Government can say what it likes, Peter, but there's going to be a General Strike. No railways, no buses, no coal, no steel—no petrol, no fuel . . ." he paused dramatically. "And no newspapers. Nothing to keep the country going or keep it informed—except the B.B.C. We'll probably be picketed ourselves, so we'll have to keep a skeleton staff on the premises, and you'd better rig up a studio in Barton Street as a temporary H.Q. If the P.M. wants to broadcast to the nation he can do it from my study. I'm going round to the Admiralty."

He called to Miss Nash: "Ring my mother, will you? Tell her she's to catch the overnight express. I'll meet her at King's Cross."

Miss Nash couldn't resist a faint smile which broadened as she saw Peter's look of almost open disbelief.

Peter said, "Extraordinary! He's got to have his mother with him! She's got to be brought from Balmoral, like Queen Victoria!"

Muriel would have agreed with him. It was extraordinary that at a time of crisis, with the house about to be turned upside down with cables and engineers running in all directions, John had to bring his mother all the way from the comparative peace and security of Dumfries. "Is Jean coming with her?" she asked as he gulped down his porridge.

"Yes, of course. Mother can't travel alone. They might stop the train and make her walk from Newcastle."

"Then wouldn't it be better to let her stay where she is?"

"Muriel, this country is going to be in a state of siege. We don't know how long it'll go on. Mother will be safe here. Besides which, she won't want to be left out of all the excitement."

So that was it. As far as John was concerned this was all an exciting adventure, and he wanted his mother to watch him go through with it. When he was a schoolboy playing rugger—he was too tall and gangling to be much good—a try meant nothing unless his mother was watching. Muriel was willing to stand on the touchline and cheer, but she knew she could only be second best. "I'll tell Winnie to put Jean in her usual room," was all she said, and John, hat in hand and off to see the leaders of the T.U.C. said, "Good, expect me when you see me."

She waved him goodbye and then sat for a moment enjoying another cup of coffee, while Winnie cleared away.

"Will your father go on strike, Winnie?"

"Sure to," said Winnie. "And knowing him, he'll be on the picket line." Winnie's father worked as a van driver for Odhams and was a Shop Steward.

"What will you do?"

Winnie laughed. "Me? Nothing. I shan't go on strike, I promise you."

"I'm glad ot that, because we're going to need you. Will you make up two more beds. Mrs Reith's coming."

The doorbell rang and Winnie answered. She admitted a rather shy policeman. "I just called to tell you that you'll have a policeman on the door from now on Ma'am."

Muriel said thankyou as though he'd delivered a parcel, and the door closed. Then she looked at him through the window. He was standing at the bottom of the steps. What an amazing thing—they were being guarded.

She rang her sister Sylvia to tell her. Sylvia wasn't in the least impressed. "I'm going to drive an ambulance," she said. "I shall be out and about—in the thick of it I expect. What are you going to do?"

Muriel was about to say, "Nothing", when she thought of Winnie. It seemed rather feeble. "I haven't decided yet."

"You can drive a lorry like you did in the war, can't you?"

"Yes, I suppose so. Things aren't that bad are they?"

"They will be," her sister assured her. "In a way I rather hope so."

Muriel rang off. What was she going to do? She hadn't thought of doing anything at all—now she'd have to or be made to look silly. John wouldn't approve—he'd say she was taking sides. She decided that whatever she did, she would keep it a secret.

She needn't have worried. John was so busy preparing for the conflict he hardly noticed whether it was night or day. He worked round the clock—with only one thought in mind—to keep the B.B.C. on the air. The enemy was government ineptitude and red tape, quite as much as union pickets. Before action could be taken to protect a few power stations essential to the transmitters, John had to provide a complete list of nearly every power station in the kingdom. He did this immediately and took the list round to Downing Street by hand. There he was confronted by the Post Master General and the heads of the Admiralty who had taken upon themselves the role of censor. John secured permission to keep his transmitters working 24 hours a day with news bulletins every hour.

It was one thing to secure permission, another to provide a 24-hour service. Peter solved the problem by connecting all stations permanently to London and London to Barton Street. Virtually at the flick of a switch, the Prime Minister could speak to the world from John's study.

To Mrs Reith the prospect of Mr Baldwin actually sitting in her son's study was like a fairy tale come true. To Muriel it was awesome. She tried to explain her nervousness to John. "I'm not like you—I'm just ordinary. You find it perfectly natural to be with Prime Ministers and those sort of people. I feel lost—wondering where I am and where all the things I knew before I got married have gone to."

"You want to feel at home, that's all. Well your home's here, with me, so you've nothing to worry about." He ended the conversation before it had had time to begin. That was his way. "Just try and forget about yourself, and treat the Prime Minister like a very welcome guest when he comes."

He glanced at the clock. Muriel was panic-stricken. "When he comes?" she repeated. "You mean he's coming soon?"

"No, but I'm expecting a telephone call from him at any minute."

They were in the middle of tea when the call came. John got up abruptly and went to take it in the study. He returned only seconds later. "Well, it's a General Strike. I suggested he broadcast to the nation, but he wants to hold himself in reserve, as he puts it."

"Are you going to do it, John?" his mother asked.

"Yes." He resumed his seat and helped himself to a scone.

"When?" asked Jean.

"Six o'clock."

"How you can sit there so calmly? . . ."

"There's no need to get excited, Jean. Everything's been prepared. All I have to do is sit in front of the microphone and wait for the green light. Oh, and I've got to think of a personal message from the Prime Minister," he added.

"John enjoys a crisis," said Jean.

"I admit I enjoy the opportunity a crisis provides—in this case to speak to the Nation, and for the Nation." He got up and left the room, taking his cup of tea with him. Really, he thought, at a time like this Jean might have the sense to keep her mouth shut. What an irritating woman his sister was . . .

At six o'clock John went on the air.

"The General Strike has begun. The Prime Minister has asked us to broadcast a personal message to the nation. Keep steady. Remember that peace on earth come to men of good will."

John waited for a moment. The red light flicked on and off. He looked up at his father's photograph over the mantelpiece. How many times had he seen his father mount the pulpit steps as the congregation sang the last verses of the "Old Hundredth"? How often seen him open the Bible and remove the notes from his sermon, then carefully place his watch on the ledge in front of him to remind him not to speak for more than fifteen minutes? Seen him bow his head in prayer and then as the congregation waited silently . . . "In the name of the father, the Son and Holy Ghost, Amen"? So many sermons, a lifetime of Christian teaching . . .

Yet on May 1st, 1926, John had given his personal message to more people than his father had preached to in a lifetime.

"Peace on earth comes to men of goodwill."

He bowed his head and said, "Amen."

At last John was where he wanted to be and where he believed he should be—at the centre of events. This was far better than being in the Cabinet, he reflected. In the Cabinet he would have to go along with the others and take his orders from the Prime Minister, but as head of the B.B.C. he was his own master, and with no newspapers he could dictate his own terms. Baldwin accepted the situation, knowing that John accepted his authority as the elected leader of the country. But Mr Winston Churchill had very different ideas. He wanted to commandeer the B.B.C. in the national interest.

The first John heard of this was when he called at Number 10 to explain the reasons behind his refusal to let the Archbishop of Canterbury broadcast.

"I do not think it proper that the B.B.C. should be used as a soap box."

Churchill frowned. "The Archbishop is hardly a tub thumper, Mr Reith."

"I have nothing against the Archbishop, he's extremely well intentioned, I have no doubt, but so are a hundred other people."

"Personally I don't think Mr Reith should be placed in the position of having to decide who shall speak and what shall be said," said Churchill. "I think that the B.B.C. should be commandeered and that I should speak to the nation this evening."

"You think you should take over my job, Mr Churchill?" John leant on the mantelpiece, deliberately unperturbed by the man who so dominated his colleagues.

"You've done a good job, you're doing a good job, Mr Reith. But I believe you should accept a degree of censorship."

"Naturally, I wouldn't wish to broadcast anything which might inflame the situation," replied John carefully. "But you said you wanted to make a personal appeal."

"Mr Churchill is, after all, Chancellor of the Exchequer," said Baldwin.

"I don't propose to make a political broadcast as Chancellor, Prime Minister." Churchill was irritated at Baldwin's specious intervention. "I intend to warn the working man of the misery which will be the lot of all those who participate in this monstrous strike, and to advertise *The British Gazette* which I shall personally publish tomorrow." He leaned back in his chair and gazed up at the almost grotesquely tall young Scotsman who seemed quite unconscious of his oddity. "What's your objection to that, Mr Reith?"

"No objection, sir. Except that most people trust the B.B.C. to speak the truth."

"I don't propose to lie."

"Nevertheless, the people don't want dope."

"Dope?" What was the man talking about?

"Once they know that the B.B.C. has been commandeered and is being manipulated by you . . ."

"I don't want to manipulate," retorted Churchill. "I want to be sure that the people are left in no doubt as to the position of His Majesty's Government."

"But the strikers have the right to know their own position as well. They pay the same licence fee."

"They won't pay that while they're on strike!"

John refused to be drawn. He admired Churchill as a man of action, but he wasn't going to be brow-beaten. "What do you think, Prime Minister?" he asked politely.

Baldwin sucked at his pipe. "Mr Reith, are you saying that if the strike is succeeding, you're going to broadcast that information?"

"I must. If Glasgow has no trains running, the people can see that for themselves. If there's no coal in Durham or steel in Sheffield, and no fish in Grimsby—the news will be broadcast. It's no good telling them it's snowing if the sun is shining in at the window."

"You're on the side of the miners, is that it?" asked Baldwin bluntly.

"Aren't we all?"

"No, we are not!" Churchill rose angrily and walked over to John, looking closely at him as though examining the face of a grandfather clock.

"I've been told you were wounded in the war."

"Yes, sir, in the head." He turned his hollow cheek for Churchill to get a good look and added, "But my present attitude is not traceable thereto."

"But you're aware that it is the duty of this Government to keep essential services going and to preserve the life and liberty of the subject?"

"As I said before, Mr Churchill, the B.B.C. will broadcast all Government orders and communications."

"But not a personal communication from the Chancellor of the Exchequer."

"Not on this occasion."

It was obvious to John that Churchill the politician and statesman was having a severe inward tussle with Churchill the Home Secretary and former victor of the siege of Sidney Street. For John there was no inward conflict. He knew he was right.

"Mr Churchill, I appreciate your point of view. But I believe that the voice they hear coming out of their wireless sets must be the one they have grown fond of, the one they know and trust— sincere and impartial, and totally independent."

"Yours," said Churchill.

"The B.B.C.'s," said John.

Churchill made no answer. He turned to Mr Baldwin. "Excuse me, Prime Minister, I must take my hat and my leave—as Wordsworth said. He was another tall fellow—another 'Wuthering Height'. I've been interested to meet you, Mr Reith."

"It's mutual," rejoined John.

After Churchill had gone.

"I don't think he likes me."

"Oh he enjoys a fight." Baldwin added a word of warning. "The only trouble is that once he regards you as his enemy, you can never be his friend."

John didn't care. He knew that Baldwin liked him, and Baldwin was the Prime Minister. He didn't pretend to under- stand Churchill, much less realise that in the swings and roundabouts of politics, a man will wait twenty years to stick the knife in.

If John did not foresee that his honourable stance for freedom and truth would one day preclude him from all hope of high office, Muriel certainly didn't expect that by helping out in a soup kitchen, she would call down upon her head the full weight of John's wrath.

"Surely you can see that by giving food out on the picket lines, you can be accused of helping the strikers?"

"Why shouldn't I help the strikers?"

"Because you're my wife, and as such you must remain impartial."

"I'm married to you—not the B.B.C."

"Don't you see—I am the B.B.C., Musie. That's not said in conceit—there's nobody else that the public can recognise and identify."

"But these workers are nothing to do with you, John. They work for Uncle William and Daddy!"

"You mean to tell me you're aiding and abetting the workers at Odhams?" John was outraged.

"Yes. You're impartial on one side, and I'm impartial on the other—that makes it even."

"There's no logic in that."

Muriel thought she'd done rather well. Perhaps she'd gained courage from serving soup alongside Mrs Philip Snowden the Labour leader's wife. She went on. "They asked me to tell you that they've left bales of paper in the road so that the *Worker's Gazette* can be published as well as the Government paper."

"They asked you to . . .!" This was too much. "Muriel, why have you done this?"

"Because I wanted to."

"But why didn't you tell me?"

"Because I knew you'd say no."

"If you knew I'd say no, why did you do it?"

"Because I wanted to. It's fun. Why do I always have to do what you want?"

"Because I happen to be right!"

There could be no argument about that, but Muriel was nevertheless trying to think of one when the telephone rang. John answered:

"Reith here."

"Mr Reith, I want you to listen carefully." It was Churchill—useless for anyone to pretend he couldn't recognise the voice.

"Yes, Mr Churchill." He put his hand over the mouthpiece and called out to Muriel, "You're not to go back Muriel—I forbid it!"

Muriel paused at the front door, then sat down on a stool. She couldn't go on with the quarrel while Mr Churchill was speaking.

John could hear a regular thump and thud of machinery down the telephone. Churchill's voice came through faintly. "You can hear that, can't you, Reith?"

"Yes, I can."

"Do you know what it is?"

"No, sir," said John.

"That is the sound of a printing press. It is printing the first issue of the *Westminster Gazette* which will be distributed throughout the land—in spite of you and your father-in-law!"

"My father-in-law? You mean Mr Odhams?"

Muriel looked at him uneasily.

"Yes. He has refused to publish for us, and you have refused to broadcast—like father like son-in-law I suppose."

"I haven't refused to broadcast, sir. There's a news bulletin every hour which contains every Government directive."

"Mr Reith, I want you to send down an engineer with a microphone, and let the nation hear the sound of the *Gazette* rolling off the printing presses. The voice of the Government cannot and will not be silenced."

"Mr Churchill, I told you that I cannot take sides by broadcasting propaganda."

"This isn't propaganda—there'll be no human voice, only the sound of the machinery speaking for itself."

He was obviously furious, but John persisted. "And immediately afterwards, am I to broadcast the silence of the shipyards and factories?" he asked.

"You do what you damned well like, Reith, but send a man

down here at once—at once, do you hear?"

"I hear you, Mr Churchill, and the answer is 'No, I will not!'"

He heard the receiver go click. He sat on the hall chest for a moment, the telephone between his knees. Muriel went over to him and put her arm round his shoulder—he looked so desperately tired. He looked round at her as though she was a stranger.

"You heard what I said to Mr Churchill, Muriel—I cannot take sides. What's good enough for Churchill's good enough for you."

He got up and went into his study and closed the door.

Baldwin sent word by special messenger. "I shall broadcast to the nation myself tomorrow—with your permission of course."

The strike had been on for a week, long enough for the general public to feel the effects without being hurt by them. Bitterness had not yet taken hold, and when John accompanied the Prime Minister from Downing Street to his home, the large police escort was almost unnecessary.

Baldwin remarked to John: "I think the T.U.C. will soon give in, but I fear the miners will fight on."

"So would I if I had to live on 25/- a week."

"I didn't know you were a Socialist, Reith."

"I don't use my vote, sir."

A man in the street saw Baldwin and waved a fist and shouted something.

"But you're on the side of the working man?"

"I worked as an engineer on the factory floor in Glasgow before the war. Up at five and home thirteen hours later—then two hours' evening classes. That went on for five long, weary years. I can find it in my heart to sympathise with the British working man, sir."

Baldwin liked John Reith more every time he met him. He was one of the few men who could always be relied upon to give a straight and unequivocal reply to a question. He was looking forward to making his broadcast—a comparatively new experience—confident that the man beside him would do everything possible to ensure its success, whether or not he agreed with his politics.

When they arrived at Number 6, Peter was in attendance to make sure that there were no technical slip-ups. He'd just returned from a prolonged meeting in Brussels to agree on European wavelengths. His plans had been accepted by the directors of the European networks and were awaiting final approvals from the twelve governments involved. After a year of negotiation and intrigue, Peter was glad to get back to being a working Chief Engineer.

He was adjusting the microphone on John's desk when the Prime Minister walked in. John introduced them and hurried off to fetch his mother. He knew she was longing to meet Mr Baldwin, whom she greatly admired. He found her in her bedroom, with Muriel skulking beside her. Luckily Jean had gone off to spend the evening with Robert who had got himself a job driving a tram. Presumably he was even now collecting the fares . . .

"Mr Baldwin's here, Mother. Come and meet him."

Mother got up eagerly, while Muriel looked round as though searching for the fire escape. "You won't want me, will you?" she asked.

"Of course I will. Don't be so daft, Musie. You are hostess to the Prime Minister. He is going to sit at your husband's desk and appeal to the British people!"

They came down the stairs. Muriel lagged behind. "I'm sure he's much too busy, John."

He turned on her with a guttural whisper. "Musie, this is one of the great moments of history! I'm part of it and so are you!"

He led the way into the study. Peter was telling the Prime Minister about plans for the Wireless Union to hold next year's big conference in Washington, and bemoaning the fact that the Russians were still not members and therefore pinching all the best wavelengths. To Mr Baldwin, wavelengths were more to do with a day at the seaside than international relations, and he gladly broke off the conversation to shake hands with old Mrs Reith and Muriel. Mrs Reith expressed great confidence in his leadership, and Muriel asked him if he'd like something to eat or a glass of sherry. Mr Baldwin said he'd just have a smoke, if she didn't object, and Muriel said that John was always smoking in the study and that Mr Baldwin could do whatever he liked. At which John suggested that she take Mother into the drawing room and that they listen to the broadcast there.

"Be sure you come in afterwards and tell us how it went," said Mr Baldwin politely, and the two ladies departed for the drawing room as though they were Victorian spinsters banished from male society while great issues were being discussed. At least that's how it seemed to Muriel. Mrs Reith took up a position by the study door and insisted that she would rather hear the broadcast through the keyhole. Useless for Muriel to explain that if she heard anything at all it would only be from the wireless set in the drawing room. But she turned the volume up and her mother-in-law sat in the hall and listened to some light music.

Inside the study, Baldwin settled into an easy chair and prepared to light his pipe. He handed John four typewritten sheets of paper. "Have a look at this tripe—see what you think of the end."

John obliged happily. There was nothing he liked better than advising Prime Ministers about what to say in their speeches— except making the speeches himself, of course. Baldwin was instinctively aware of his young protégé's predilection, he was used to fostering the talents of others and making use of them. Some worked best if offered preferment as a bait, others wanted honours . . . John Reith wanted power and influence, and the opportunity to guide the affairs of the nation.

"I'd like to finish on a personal note," he said. "See if you can think of something."

John read the speech to the end and glanced at the clock. There were still 8½ minutes. He rememberd the last personal message from Baldwin that he'd delivered on his behalf. "You haven't said you're a man of peace and honour. Perhaps. . . ?" He looked across at the Prime Minister who as usual waited a moment or two before replying. This gave the impression that all his replies were considered opinions.

"Something on those lines, yes. Thank you, Reith. Put it down—whatever you like."

John sat down at the desk in front of the microphone and took out his pen.

"I hope you've got a legible hand," said Baldwin with a smile.

"Rather cramped, sir, but I'll write big." He wrote direct onto the typescript, then spoke into the microphone.

"Peter, shall we try a voice level?"

"Ready when you are."

John looked across at the Prime Minister. "Will this do, sir?" He leaned towards the microphone and read out what he'd just written. "I am longing and working and praying for peace, but I won't compromise the dignity of the constitution."

"Excellent, Reith, excellent. Can I just add a few words of my own?" He took John's place at the desk, borrowed his pen and wrote a final paragraph. The clock ticked on—five minutes to go. He removed his pipe. "There—that should do the trick."

"Would you like to try a voice level now, sir?"

"Certainly. What shall I say?"

"Whatever you like, sir, providing there are no swear words," Peter spoke on the loudspeaker.

"I'll do my best, Captain Eckersley. May I take the opportunity of congratulating you on the way you run the technical side of the B.B.C.? If there's anything I can do to help—don't hesitate to let me know."

"Well you could start by giving us a ten-year Charter sir," Peter's voice boomed out.

John looked anxiously at the Prime Minister. He felt that mention of the Charter at this moment was almost like blackmail.

Baldwin spoke into the microphone. "Thank you, Captain Eckersley. Providing my voice comes over clearly, I shall certainly not forget the Charter."

"That sounded fine. Keep it like that and don't lean back sir."

Where angels fear to tread, thought John. That was Peter all over, and he always seemed to get away with it.

It was almost nine o'clock. John stood next to the desk. "Don't worry, sir. Talk as though you're talking to me. When I get the signal, I'll lean over and make the announcement and you go ahead when you're ready." He put on his headphones.

A moment later, "This is London calling on all stations. The Right Honourable Stanley Baldwin, Prime Minister."

John tiptoed back to his chair.

Baldwin began. "Good evening."

John listened in admiration. Not because of the skill with which Baldwin's speech balanced so brilliantly upon a tightrope of moderation, but because of the manner of its delivery. He seemed to be speaking from the heart. "The man's a born broadcaster," thought John. He listened a little longer, and then suddenly had qualms about his own contribution. "Dignity of the constitution." This was no time to stand on dignity. He got up and moved silently over to the desk. The Prime Minister didn't look up or stop as John removed the last sheet of paper from under his hand. He crossed out "dignity" and wrote "Safety and security" instead.

Hardly had he resumed his seat when he had second thoughts on that too, but by then it was too late. The final peroration had begun.

"I am longing and working and praying for peace, but I will not compromise the safety and security of the constitution. You placed me in power eighteen months ago with an overwhelming majority—have I done anything to forfeit that confidence? Can you not trust me to ensure a square deal and secure even justice between man and man?"

John stepped forward. "That was the Prime Minister, the Right Honourable Stanley Baldwin, speaking to you from Westminster.'

The door opened and Mrs Reith came in. She went straight over to John without a word, and reached up and kissed him. "That was wonderful, John—wonderful!"

She became aware of the Prime Minister who'd stood up politely as she entered. "And I must congratulate Mr Baldwin too. That was a beautiful speech—worthy of the occasion."

Baldwin took her hand. "You must be very proud of your son, Mrs Reith."

"Yes, I am, very."

John looked over his mother's shoulder. Muriel was hovering at the door. "Come in, Muriel. Tell us all what you thought of it."

"Oh I heard every word," said Muriel shyly. "Would you like to stay for supper, Mr Baldwin?"

"Oh thank you, no. My dear wife will worry about me if I don't go straight back to Number 10."

After the Prime Minister had departed, they were joined for supper by Peter and his wife Stella. "You look rather pallid, Stella," said John. "You should take Virol."

Stella gave a pallid smile, and Muriel changed the subject. John could be very tactless. He knew perfectly well that all Stella was suffering from was Peter—or perhaps lack of Peter. He was away from home even more than John.

"I thought it was very nice the way the Prime Minister said he had to get back home to his wife, didn't you?" She looked at Peter, hoping that he might be prodded into saying something kind to Stella.

"I thought he was pathetic," said John. "And do you know, he actually struck a match while I was making the announcement!"

17

Once the miners had capitulated, John broadcast messages of peace and reconciliation from the Prime Minister and the King, and devoted the rest of the year to securing a new Charter which would give the B.B.C. "Monopoly under God", as he called it to the Crawford Commission of Enquiry.

"Gentlemen, I am asking for a monopoly—not under the State, but under God. Our responsibility is to carry into the greatest numbers of homes, everything that is best in every department of human knowledge, behaviour and achievement."

"Won't you sit down, Mr Reith?" asked the Chairman plaintively.

"I like to stand, sir," hands clutching his lapels—shades of Lord Birkenhead. "The B.B.C. must be accepted as a permanent and essential part of the machinery of civilisation. Gentlemen, there is at hand a mighty instrument to banish ignorance and misery and to enrich the sum total of human well-being. The sole concern of those to whom the stewardship is given—by accident—is to ensure that those basic ideals should be sealed and safeguarded in this Charter, so that broadcasting may play its part in the destiny of the human race."

This sort of peroration, combined with detailed reports, carried all before it. When the Press tried to prevent this further encroachment on their preserves, John attacked with Calvinistic spirit, not only the Barons, but the whole of the Establishment: "Pinhead Press, with no regard for veracity, concerned only with their own power and profits; politicians who see broadcasting only as the means of disseminating their own predilections; the rich and the royal, who imagine their own prerogatives and

preserves to be threatened, are angered because their puny
spleens and gibes have fallen on an impervious and indifferent
B.B.C.! We sail uncharted in treacherous seas, where never sail
was carried before, and we shall continue to seek to fly the flag
of independence and integrity at our masthead!"

Such a speech enlivened many a dull city banquet, but earned
John the secret enmity of a good few of the politicians and
journalists who sniggered at what they took to be references to
people like Rothermere and Beaverbrook and Churchill.

John, busily sailing his uncharted sea, ignored the petty squalls
and kept his eye on the compass, and the compass was fixed to
the North Star. And the North Star was, of course, fixed by the
Almighty, so how could John Reith go wrong?

Charles Carpendale, having served a lifetime in the Navy,
knew very well! When Baldwin offered John a knighthood, the
Admiral warned him to be very circumspect before accepting.
"They'll say you got it for helping the Conservative Government
break the General Strike."

"In that case I'd better refuse. On the other hand, a knighthood
will place the Director General of the B.B.C. on top of the pile
where he belongs." John had learned from his brief secretaryship
of the Parliamentary Unionists, that honours are distributed in
line with the pecking order. He wanted a knighthood for the
honour of the B.B.C., and a decent one too. When he looked
round and saw the kind of people who got knighthoods he'd
almost rather wait till he got a peerage.

He waited until the Prime Minister himself rang him up and
asked him. "I'm personally asking you to accept a knighthood for
the impartial and patriotic manner in which you handled
broadcasting during the national crisis which, but for your
calmness and steadiness, might have led this nation into a civil
war."

"Thank you, Prime Minister, I accept the honour with gratitude on behalf of the B.B.C."

He went home to tell Muriel, and she was thrilled.

"Mind you, Baldwin's a cunning old fox. He knows which side
his bread's buttered."

John and Muriel went along to Savoy Hill as usual, to greet the

New Year. He'd experienced miserable New Year's Eves, lonely ones, happy ones—but New Year's Eve 1926 was the first triumphant one. At the stroke of midnight he announced to his staff of 600: "The old B.B.C. is dead. Long live the Royal Chartered Corporation!" And he gave Muriel a kiss and whispered, "Happy New Year, your Ladyship!"

The next morning he read the headline: "Baldwin honours the first Director General of the B.B.C. Sir John Reith—Knight of the General Strike!"

The same sort of jibes were in all the newspapers. John banged them down on his desk.

"Don't get ruffled, John. It's only a warning salvo across your bows," said the Admiral.

John picked up the phone. "I think I shall fire a warning salvo across Gladstone Murray's bows."

Captain Gladstone Murray in his Publicity Office, heard the phone ring three times. The Director General must want him. It was all part of John's policy of avoiding intermediaries and going straight for the man with the ball.

"Morning, Sir John, Murray here. What can I do for you?"

Murray was, like Peter Eckersley, an Air Force Captain, but Canadian. He'd come from the *Daily Express* to the B.B.C., and had his work cut out placating the "pinhead Press" whenever John got on the wrong side of Fleet Street—which was pretty often.

"Will you come to my office, please, at once."

The phone clicked down. Murray wasn't panic-stricken as others were who received the triple summons from on high, but he didn't waste time. Savoy Hill was such an intimate place, that it only took him a couple of minutes to walk along the passage to John's office. John didn't waste time either.

"Murray you've got to do something about this." He thrust the papers towards him.

"I've already been on to them."

"Well get on to them again. Tell your friend Beaverbrook that I'm not one of his miserable civil servants, knighted for deeds of heroism during the General Strike!"

"It's only the usual gang, Sir John."

"I daresay, but they do so much damage. They couldn't stop us becoming a Corporation, so now that we are, they're like rats gnawing at the foundations. And Baldwin's so sly. Churchill goes for you with an axe, but Baldwin! He wants the B.B.C. for his own purposes, just as much as they all do."

Carpendale intervened. "John be fair, he's given us the Charter. We're secure for ten years."

"We're still under the thumb of the wretched Postmaster General—he collects our licence fee . . . Every time I post a letter I feel sick!"

"I'll see what I can do," said Murray.

"That's no use. You tell me now—who are you going to speak to?"

"Beaverbrook. I'll say you want to discuss your plans for the B.B.C., and would like to have dinner with him."

"I don't want to discuss anything with him."

"I'm sure you do really, John. After all, you're both sons of the Manse. You can talk about religion."

John gave his reluctant consent. "Oh very well. But remember, your job is to prevent this sort of thing, not mend the fences afterwards. I accepted that knighthood at the personal request of the Prime Minister and to strengthen my position with the new Board of Governors!" He closed the door on the Head of Public Relations.

"Is Muriel pleased?" asked the Admiral.

"She always is. She'll make a good milch cow, that's what I tell her. She thinks she's going to have a baby, but there's no sign, and I haven't got the time."

"You should make time, if that's what Muriel wants." The Admiral was like a father to both of them.

Miss Nash came in with a pile of letters, and John looked in his diary.

"I've been asked to visit Germany as guest of the Deutchrund-funk—open their new radio station. I may take Muriel with me." He found the date. "The first Board Meeting of the new Governors is on the 4th, by the way. Has everybody been notified, Miss Nash?"

"Yes, Sir John." She put the mail on his desk.

"What's all this?"

"Letters of congratulation."

He started to look through them in a desultory manner. "What do you think of our new Board of Governors, Miss Nash?"

"They seem very representative, Sir John."

"Representative of what? Middle of the road mediocrity—safety first. I begged Baldwin to keep Gainford—he may have been yellow at times, but . . ."

"Gainford yellow?" Carpendale was constantly amazed at John's ability to damn his associates with one word. "Gainford's a coal owner. Baldwin couldn't possibly keep him as Chairman with Mrs Snowden."

"At least Gainford isn't tied to the interstices of Whitehall by yards of red tape."

"Oh come on—you'll have Clarendon eating out of your hand, like the rest of us."

John wasn't convinced. Clarendon had been an assistant in the Dominion Office. John had seen him in action when he met the Postmaster General. He was a master at putting out red carpets and saluting the right person, but he wouldn't say boo to a goose, let alone a Cabinet Minister.

"He's another one you should ask out to dinner," suggested Carpendale.

"Good idea. Fix a date and you'd better come too. Ask Mrs Snowden at the same time."

"All right. I'll make it tomorrow or the day after."

"So long as it's before the meeting."

"Aye, aye sir," said Carpendale. He held the door open for Jo Stanley as she brought in some more letters. It was her first day as Miss Nash's assistant.

"How many more of them are there?" asked John.

"About 150 all together."

"Great Scott! Take them out of here. Put them in a box and I'll take them home with me. Muriel can sort them—give her something to do."

Jo Stanley gladly relinquished the laborious task. Many of the writers were obviously personal friends and acquaintances of the family who would require more than a formal acknowledgement.

Muriel was equally glad to have a chance to do more for John than attend official functions which she detested. He didn't seem to mind spending a whole evening with complete strangers, and returned full of gossip and comment. She'd much rather listen to him describe it all than endure it in person.

While he got ready to escort Lord Clarendon and Mrs Snowden to the Savoy, Muriel painstakingly sorted through the letters of congratulation, putting aside the ones she knew John would want to answer himself. Almost at once she spotted Charlie's handwriting. She thought for a moment that she should put it on one side for John to open, but to do so would be to arouse his suspicions. How did she know it was from Charlie? Had he told her he was going to write? Why didn't she open it like all the others?

She could hear John singing loudly as he forced his stiff shirt into his trousers and manouevred the gold studs. She opened the letter. "Dear John," she read, "May I take this opportunity of adding my voice to all those, who like me, enjoy listening to the B.B.C. and are delighted that you have received the honour of knighthood which you so richly deserve. Yours Sincerely, Charles Bowser."

She looked at it, sent from the family cottage near Godalming. He was probably staying with his parents on his own—he wouldn't dare write if Maisie were around. She'd met Maisie once or twice for a cup of tea at Fortnum's, and she knew how she and Charlie were getting on—everything was fine, according to Maisie. She was expecting her first baby in the Spring. Mrs Reith kept up with the family and hoped that one day they could all get together again, but "John is such a difficult man".

Muriel heard him coming downstairs and put the letter among the other family ones. He was carrying his jacket and waistcoat and did a little dance like a scarecrow. "My braces burst," he said. "I'm like a puppet!"

"Oh dear, I meant to get you another pair."

"They'll last the evening. If they don't I'm sure Clarendon will oblige with an elastic band."

Muriel held his jacket while he put on his waistcoat. "Mrs Snowden will have a safety pin I'm sure."

"I wouldn't trust her with my trousers," John said. "According to Ramsay MacDonald, she's the one that wears them in the Snowden household. He rang me this morning to offer his congratulations, so I took the opportunity of complaining at his choice. He said it was nothing to do with him and he was really very cross. He said he wouldn't wish Mrs Snowden on his worst enemy. When he was in Number 10 he could hear her next door in Number 11 screaming at her husband. He said 'Poor old Philip, if he expects to be Chancellor of the Exchequer next time round, he'll have to agree to keep Ethel in a soundproof room!' "

John laughed and glanced at Muriel's pile of opened letters.

"There's a telegram from Jean," she said, waiting for him to notice Charlie's.

"I expect Mother paid for that."

"All my family seem to have written." His hand picked up Charlie's letter. He let it dangle from his fingers like a dead rat, as though he were holding the *Daily Express* or some newspaper that he hated. "That one's from Charlie," she said faintly.

"What's he say?"

"Congratulations."

John read the letter in silence. Then he commented: "What a long and involved sentence. He never could write English." And he tore it up into small pieces.

"John! What did you do that for?"

He dropped the pieces into the waste paper basket. "I've arranged to meet Clarendon and Mrs Snowden at my office, so that they can be shown round before we go over to the Savoy."

He put on his overcoat. Muriel helped him automatically. "John darling, it's three years since . . ."

"Four."

"Four then. You haven't seen him for four years. He's changed, you've changed . . ." She took his hands. "This is like an olive branch. Why can't you forgive? Why can't you ever forgive and forget?"

"Charlie?" There was a look of such pain in his eyes. Then he said quite lightly," I will forget, I do forget, I have forgotten."

Muriel refused to be put down like a child. "I don't understand you, John. All these other letters from important people we hardly know and who don't care tuppence for us—you'll read them, and keep them, and stick some of them in your scrapbook. But the one from your best friend—your only friend—you tear that up!"

John looked slightly irritated. "Muriel, it's typical of you to start an argument just as I'm trying to collect my thoughts. It's most important that I start off on the right foot with the new Chairman."

"John, Charlie was my friend too! So was Maisie."

"Jezebel!"

"They were friends. I need friends, and I haven't got any."

"You've plenty of relatives. Doris Philips and the Moirs and Uncle Will Odhams and all."

He turned to go, but she suddenly clung to him.

"Oh come on Musie, I've got to go."

"I'm lonely! I'm lonely, John!"

He was surprised to see tears in her eyes. He suddenly felt guilty to be going out and leaving her.

"We'll have friends round," he said quietly. "We'll make friends—new friends. I'll make more of an effort in that direction." She smiled up at him and he kissed her. "But not Maisie . . . And not Charlie. Never."

John hurried through the theatre-going traffic to keep his appointment. He soon forgot about Charlie and Jezebel. He'd suffered a momentary pang, that was all, and was pleased with his reactions. In a year or two there'd be no pangs—happy memories and no regrets. He passed the Cenotaph. Perhaps it'd be like the war—there was no sadness now, only a curiosity and still an anger at the inefficiency and waste. If a commercial company had run the war half as badly, they'd have been out of business within weeks. He must remember to ask Muriel if she'd like to go round the battlefields this summer. They could go and see her fiancé's grave, and then go on to Noyelles where John'd been wounded. Muriel would probably prefer to sit on the beach at Guernsey, but she could always go to Southwick later on. Yes he'd do that. It would amuse him to take Muriel on a guided tour and maybe find the actual spot. Then he remembered Charlie all over again. He remembered lying on the bottom of the trench, covered in blood, and writing a note to his mother, and one to Charlie and then passing out again. So much to remember—so much to forget.

Plater saluted him at the door, still there—nearly seven o'clock. Kilroy took him up in the lift.

"You must be due for a bonus, aren't you, Kilroy?"

"Oh yes, sir. Say the word and I'll be up to your office like a Jack-in-the-box."

"I'll see about it."

He came out of the lift and walked along the passage to his office. Five years since Kilroy first took him up in the lift. He should have had a bonus at Christmas! What the blazes was Carpendale doing? He'd have a word with him—not now . . .

He opened his office door. Carpendale was already there, looking after Lord Clarendon. Thank God for the Admiral; thank God for Miss Nash. "Lord Clarendon—so sorry I'm late—how are you, sir?"

They shook hands. "Very glad to be here," said Clarendon, "And looking forward to a lot of hard work."

"Oh well . . ." John shot a glance at Carpendale who gave a twitch of one eyebrow. "Don't go, Miss Nash. Miss Nash will be your secretary, Lord Clarendon."

"Oh," his lordship seemed put out. "I thought I'd have to provide my own."

"No, no, Miss Nash will do for both of us. She was recommended to me by Lloyd George."

"Lloyd George, Hm." He looked Miss Nash up and down as though he knew of the late Prime Minister's predilection for pinching bottoms and wondered if Miss Nash had suffered at his hands. "Well, I'm sure we'll get on very well, Miss Nash."

"Thank you, sir."

John felt guilty that he'd asked her to stay late in order to meet the new Chairman. Lord Clarendon dismissed her. "When Mrs Snowden comes, tell her I'm in here."

"Then you'd better get off home," said John. He disliked Clarendon giving orders to his secretary. And he disliked the way the man was now peering at his father's photograph like an antique dealer looking for a signature. "Pity about Mrs Snowden, but I expect her husband's glad to get her out of the house."

"I gather she's the Postmaster General's choice." Clarendon adopted the tone of good-natured reprimand.

"Och, that explains it. Trust him to give us the most cantankerous suffragette since Joan of Arc!"

"Oh, I don't agree at all." He took shelter beside the Admiral. "She's a Socialist, of course, but I flatter myself I'm a pretty good judge of character."

"You flatter yourself—is that so?" At any rate there's no need to worry—she won't be here that often. Membership of the Board is only a very part-time occupation, as I'm sure you'll agree."

"That's not the impression I was given by the Prime Minister, quite the contrary." He smoothed his moustache. "And Mrs Snowden told me she's expecting to have an office of her own and work here the greater part of the week."

"Out of the question." John dismissed the idea.

Carpendale intervened politely. "You have an office, of course, as Chairman, sir. It's just across the passage."

"We'll leave you to furnish it in your own way. Miss Nash did all mine," John added.

"I prefer to do it myself, thank you." Clarendon was almost icy. "I'm rather fussy."

"Fussy? What's that mean?"

"I like to make up my own mind . . . In my own way, in my own time." He'd heard about the Director General, and he wasn't going to be pushed around. There was a knock on the door, and Miss Nash announced Mrs Snowden.

John lunged forward to shake the outstretched hand of Ethel Snowden, then stopped and grabbed the top of his trousers. "Damn and blast the thing!"

"I beg your pardon?"

"I'm afraid I've burst my braces, Mrs Snowden. Have you got some string, Miss Nash?"

He began to take off his jacket and waistcoat, while he introduced Admiral Carpendale. The situation appealed to John's sense of humour, but his Deputy could see that the members of

the Board were not so addicted to the Aldwych farces. It was an
inauspicious start to the evening. Useless for John to explain that
when you're six-foot-six, braces are a constant hazard. For
Clarendon it was a breach of etiquette, if not an act of gross
indecency. While for Mrs Snowden, the sight of Miss Nash—a
free and educated woman—actually being forced to sew on a
man's back button. . . ! And what made it worse was the way
John kept laughing so loudly, and she'd been told he had no
sense of humour. As the wife of a former Chancellor of the
Exchequer, she felt her dignity was affronted, and John was to
find out that she had precious little sense of humour herself.

Dinner at the Savoy reached coffee and dessert without
mishap. Mrs Snowden said that Labour would sweep the country
at the next election, and that the "Women's Peace Movement", of
which she was a leading light, would sweep the world. It wasn't
till her second cup of coffee that she mentioned the Board
Meeting the next day.

"I've got a number of things I'd like to discuss which aren't on
the agenda."

"Well as it's only the first meeting, perhaps you could have
them put on the agenda for the next one. After all, we must get
to know each other to start off with." John was being ultra-polite.

"We don't want to get the reputation of dragging our feet,"
Mrs Snowden persisted.

"Not much danger of that with you around."

Mrs Snowden refused to be sidetracked. She stirred her coffee
vigorously. "Personally I think we should have a meeting every
day—that's one of the first things I want put on the agenda."

John still remained genial. He wanted to get back to Muriel in
one piece. "If we meet every day, Mrs Snowden, from my
experience of Boards, there'll be so much hot air generated we'll
blow the place up."

Mrs Snowden was momentarily silenced, and John gave the
Admiral a nod, who said that he hoped they'd excuse him
because he wasn't as young as he used to be . . . and the party
broke up. John had not enjoyed it. His parting words to
Carpendale didn't auger well for the future. "If you ask me,
Clarendon's a weak man who mistakes obstinacy for determina-

tion. As for Mrs Snowden . . . God help the 'Women's Peace Movement' if there are many more like her!"

Carpendale drove off in his taxi—a Beardmore, John noted—and the Director General walked home. 1927 had got off to a good start. There might be a few teething troubles with the new Board of Governors, but nothing more. The stage was set for bigger and better triumphs. He never for one second imagined that by 1929, Lord Clarendon and Mrs Snowden between them, would almost drive him mad!

18

Fortunately for John, like many another "great man", the balance
of his mind didn't depend on the vagaries of his career. He had
"the devoted wife" to keep him on an even keel. And during the
rest of 1927 he saw considerably more of Muriel than he did of
the Board. Moreover, although Lord Clarendon was a constant
source of irritation, Mrs Snowden had not reached her zenith.
She had yet to return to Number 11 as the Chancellor of the
Exchequer's wife.

The B.B.C. was the model which the rest of Europe and the
Empire copied. Peter Eckersley was almost more famous than
John, and the good Carpendale was President of the International Wireless Association. All three were inundated with
invitations from all parts of the world. They took it in turns to
open conferences and radio stations, and when reunited at the
regular High Teas served at executive meetings, they planned
and organised new link-ups and outside broadcasts—more
concerts and dramas, more and more of everything. John, still
sailing his uncharted ocean, was happy with his chosen crew,
firm in his conviction that the ship he sailed had been built to his
own specifications and was the best in the world.

Muriel and he went off to France to visit the battlefields in
September. For Muriel it was a pilgrimage to her brother
Christopher's grave and to her fiancé's. For John it was a
splendid opportunity to relive the past. All in all he'd thoroughly
enjoyed his war, and he carried the diary for 1914 to 1915 with
him to prove it.

They didn't have any difficulty finding either of the graves.
The cemeteries were well mapped and catalogued, and there

were crowds of other people searching out the last resting place
of their sons and brothers and husbands. Muriel did as they did,
scooping up a little of the earth to bring home, leaving a bunch
of flowers. It was sad for her. She remembered her brother as
she knew him best. She'd had a happy childhood. They'd been a
close-knit family, centred on her father. He'd been an epileptic,
and they were used to curbing their spirits in order not to excite
him. Muriel had nurtured her natural shyness into a placidity
which could never be disturbed. If she was angry or hurt she
withdrew herself until the pain had gone.

And now she withdrew from John. She had so little that she
really seemed to own. He was all-pervading, all-powerful, almost
unaware that she had feelings and ambitions and a personality of
her own which needed to be fed and cared for just as much as
his. John didn't try to impose himself between Muriel and her
grief. He held her hand and said a prayer and recited the words
of *Abide with me*. And Muriel thought of her childhood. She was
thirty-five. She turned to John and said, "If we have a son, can
we call him Christopher?" John nodded his head and said, "Yes."
What else could he do under the circumstances? Of course he'd
have preferred to have called him George after his father, but he
didn't object to Christopher.

Having shown suitable respect for the dead, John was anxious
to visit some of his old haunts and lay a few of the ghosts which
still haunted him. At Armentiere they walked down the street
looking for the house which had been John's first billet in 1914.
It was still standing, and he felt sure that the two girls who'd
accommodated him and his NCOs so comfortably, would open
the door and welcome him in. But there was a new owner and
new paint and the paddock at the back, where John had kept his
blood mare "Sailaway", had been built on. In 1914 John had
been Transport Officer to the 5th Scottish Rifles, and had
savoured power for the first time in his life. Even his C.O. was
subject to him. He could grant or withhold the means of
sustaining life in reasonable comfort. He took full advantage of
his position. He made sure that the 5th Scottish Rifles had the
best of everything, and in return won his own independence.

He stopped suddenly and pointed to a squat pebble dashed

house: "There's H.Q. The Jerries were half a mile away—I never
saw anything of them, so I had no hatred of the enemy. As far as
I was concerned the enemy resided in that H.Q. building—
Captain Croft, the Adjutant. I never got on with my fellow
officers, I don't why—something in me I suppose."

"You got on with Colonel Thompson," Muriel reminded him.

"Ah, but that was Brighton, and I'd just fallen in love with his
driver!"

They walked back to their ancient hired car. "Captain Croft
was the bane of my life. He couldn't bear anything that wasn't by
the book—like my having the best horse in the regiment and my
men the best billets! Always complaining about the colour of my
shirts not being regulation, and the fact that I didn't march my
men up to the orderly room every time they misunderstood
some pettifogging company order. In the end he spirited my
horse away and tried to get me courtmartialled! The Brigadier
promoted me and I got my horse back, but I hated Captain
Croft— and I still do." They got back into the car. "So much for
the Battle of the Somme."

Muriel wondered how a man with so much wisdom and vision
could still retain such an elephantine memory for long-dead
injuries. He seemed to take them out and polish them to keep
them bright and shining for the moment when they could be
repaid. Perhaps that was the purpose of the diaries. From what
she'd seen of them, they were just full of what she called "old
sores and old scores".

"Nothing of the kind," John had informed her. "That diary is
living history—or history relived." Whatever that meant.

They relived more history at Bethune, where John sat at a
table, carefully chosen, and said, "You are now sitting at the
same table as Winston Churchill sat at in 1915. I was sitting at
that one over there. I'd been home on leave after a bad attack of
dysentery, got from going out in the dark and filling my bottle at
a manure heap!"

"Churchill? What was he doing?"

"Being shown round by some General or other. I was very
impressed. Odd that now these great men seem nothing. I was
full of the joys of Spring. I'd got myself posted to the Engineers. I

could hear the guns. I didn't realise, but the Battle of Loos had started."

Their car took them on to Noyelles and beyond that to a little village. They left the car and John wandered off, while Muriel sat on a wall. He was gone an hour. He came back.

"I couldn't find it."

"Find what?"

"The place where I was shot. Come and I'll show you."

Muriel accompanied him into a field of sugar beet. It was fenced round, and in one corner was the remains of a brickyard. John walked between the rows and stopped. "Somewhere in the ground there is the bullet that was meant to kill me. And somewhere in that brickyard is the empty cartridge from the sniper's rifle."

"What happened, John?"

"You can read my diary. See what a fool you've got for a husband."

She took his hand and kissed his broken cheek very gently.

Later on at the hotel in Noyelles, John gave her his diary, open at October 7th, 1915. Muriel read of how John had accompanied his C.O. to show him the damage caused by a mine explosion in the night. Rather than get his new uniform dirty, he'd walked along the top of the parapet . . .

Muriel stopped, thinking of the field of sugar beet. "The brickstack was only a hundred yards away from you John."

"I told you I was a fool."

Muriel read on. "I invited the Major to do the same. He stayed where he was, and after we'd got past some troops, I jumped down and rejoined him. I was very interested to see what work required to be done. The trench was in an awful state, the parapet blown away in places. Then I was hit. I knew it was in the head. My teeth were all smashed up. I lay down and a Wiltshire Sergeant used his field dressing. I hadn't got mine with me, as I was wearing my new tunic. I felt angry that it was covered in blood. I asked for a bit of paper. I thought I was going to die. I wrote Mother's name and address and put 'I'm all right.' Then I wrote to Charlie: 'Cheer up old boy. Johnnie.' Then I suppose I passed out."

Muriel didn't read any more. She was thinking. He thought he was going to die, so he wrote to his mother, and then he wrote to Charlie. He wrote to the people who mattered most to him.

"John," she said. "If you thought you were going to die now . . who would you write to?"

John replied at once. "I'd write to Mother, and I'd write to you, Musie. In that order!"

They spent the last two days in Boulogne, shopping for gifts to add to the souvenirs they'd collected. John enjoyed buying them—but only for other people. Not only had Mother and Jean and Winnie to be remembered, but Miss Nash and Miss Stanley and Carpendale. Then he insisted that Muriel brought back souvenirs for her father and mother and her brother, John Lynch—not Edward, who'd never been forgiven for suggesting that Muriel and Charlie danced too close together. He kept the German helmet for himself, but only to show to a dull visitor or two to break the monotony.

Miss Nash and Miss Stanley were delighted with their presents and with the cards addressed to Betty and Jo. John always retained the formalities in the office, but outside the two secretaries were treated as friends. He would expect them to stay late, putting a memorandum or report together. They'd all three be on their knees sorting the pages and stapling them together, in order that some high-placed dignitary should find the report on his desk the following morning, when he hadn't expected it for a fortnight. They'd deliver the package to the Ministry and then go out to dinner.

'Put some scent on, Miss Nash."

"I'll put it on after the Governor's Meeting, Sir John."

"Put some on now. It'll give the White Rabbit something to think about—Oh, and the Red Queen something to complain about."

As far as John was concerned, Board Meetings were like something out of *Alice in Wonderland* with the Chairman always looking at his watch, and Mrs Snowden quarrelling and complaining. John was like "Alice" in the middle, trying vainly to make sense of the mad world they inhabited.

Mrs Snowden waited impatiently for the end of the meeting and "Any Other Business", then let loose her pent up sense of outrage. "I happened to bump into Gladstone Murray in the canteen, and he calmly informed me that we are going to build ourselves a new Headquarters on the river, and had already secured the lease!"

John wondered whether he should try and explain the months of consultation with his executive management which had accompanied a search for new premises. He decided that nothing but delay and obstruction would result from allowing the Red Queen any choice in the matter. So he simply informed her. "The site's next to the Queen's Hall, and we've got the fee simple."

Mrs Snowden was mollified by the proximity to the musical Mecca of London, but the White Rabbit appeared bewildered: "Fee simple, Sir John? You mean freehold?"

"I mean 'fee simple', Mr Chairman. The property belongs to Lord Howard de Walden. As soon as the terms are known in detail, the Board can accept or reject them."

Mrs Snowden clicked her tongue. "Mr Chairman, I do think we should be told about what's going on. At the last meeting we were talking about starting a new magazine. Now I understand from Mr Gladstone Murray that it's to be called *The Listener* and that Mr Lambert has already been appointed editor. How did that happen?"

"I interviewed him and gave him the job," said John.

"Without informing anyone!"

"I informed him."

"You should have told us first."

"You had a list of the candidates, Mrs Snowden, and if I remember rightly, he was the only one you didn't object to."

The rest of the Board failed to answer Mrs Snowden's call to arms, so she changed the subject to the plight of musicians, and how underpaid they were, at which Lord Gainford was roused to say that his coal mines were losing money hand over fist and the B.B.C. had only so much money from the licence fee, and Mrs Snowden said he shouldn't believe everything he read in the Tory Press and that "our Director General" gave in to them far too easily.

"One word from Lord Beaverbrook and the programme is cancelled. The Talks Department doesn't know if it's coming or going."

"They're going," said John "Mrs Matheson is at any rate."

The Red Queen became even more agitated. "Mrs Matheson leaving? Why? This is outrageous. Just because she's a woman!"

"Not because she's a woman. She insists on getting her own way, and her work is not what it was."

And so it went on, arguing and squabbling until Mrs Snowden finally produced her ace . . . She'd had complaints from the regions that they had no autonomy and that members of the staff in Birmingham were being harassed and bullied by the London office. Suddenly John announced: "I have go to up to Birmingham to open the new studio in a fortnight. Perhaps we could all go together and see for ourselves what life is like in the Midlands."

Mrs Snowden was thrown into confusion and the meeting broke up as the Board united to plan their outing.

John asked Muriel to come with him, but she said she didn't want to travel unnecessarily.

"Why not?" asked John.

"Not just at the moment."

"Are you feeling ill?"

"No, but I think I'm having a baby."

John was surprised and said he was pleased, and went off to Birmingham, where the Board much enjoyed the round of civic receptions, while John took the opportunity of interviewing a member of the staff and sacking him. The matter was raised at the next meeting, when John produced clear evidence that the man had been using his position as contract manager to rob musicians of a part of their fees. Mrs Snowden was furious.

"You are accusing this man of bribery and corruption and not giving him the chance to defend himself!"

"Are you disputing the evidence, Mrs Snowden?"

"No. But he has a right to put his case to the Board of Governors."

"Mrs Snowden, the man has admitted his guilt, he's deeply sorry for what he has done, and very grateful that he is not being put in the dock. He has resigned and been paid a month's wages. My job is not to judge and punish, it's simply to ensure the smooth running of this enterprise."

"The fact is you've thrown this unfortunate man out of work, without one thought for the misery and suffering you've inflicted on his wife and family."

John rose to his feet. "You want to get your facts right, Mrs Snowden, before you distort them." And he left the meeting without further comment.

He realised that he'd won that particular skirmish and left the field in good array. But he was unhappy with himself. He took Muriel for a walk in the park. It was coming up to Easter, the weather was mild and the daffodils in bloom, and the ducks—his beloved ducks—squawking their love calls. "My job isn't supposed to be keeping some wretched Board happy by satisfying their desire for power and glory. It's a waste of time and energy. I'm half inclined to chuck the whole thing up and let them get on with it."

Muriel sat heavily on a park bench, while John fed the ducks. The baby was due in a month or so. She felt happy just to sit in the sunshine and watch John throwing bits of bread on the lake, trying to ensure that each bird got its fair share.

"I tell you one thing." he said vehemently. "If the Red Queen goes on like this, I'm going to tell her a few home truths."

"Oh I think that would be a great mistake," pleaded Muriel.

"Well, I shall moderate my language, but I am not going to be deflected from the task in hand." And he hurled a piece of bread into the centre of the lake. "Excalibur!" he exclaimed as a duck shot up out of the water.

19

Perhaps it was the May Day celebrations of the Labour Opposition scenting victory in the next election, or the sudden
heatwave which heralded the Christian festival of Whitsuntide,
but the next Governor's Meeting was an even more heated affair
than the last one. The Red Queen had a long list of grievances
which she wanted to discuss, but the White Rabbit was in a
hurry to get to Bournemouth. It was suggested that she should
summarise her points in a memorandum which could then be
distributed for the consideration of the rest of the Board before
the next meeting.

John had said almost nothing throughout the meeting, not
wishing to prolong it. Muriel had suffered one or two pains in
the night, and he hadn't slept.

Mrs Snowden said, "Very well. Now about the . . ."

John said, "Mr Chairman, I've drawn up next week's agenda.
Members of the Board may like to add to it. There's television,
foreign language broadcasts, and the allocation of broadcasting
time in the forthcoming election—whenever that may be."

"The sooner the better," said the Red Queen.

"I'll produce memorandi on all these subjects which you'll
receive after the Whitsuntide holiday. Now, if you'll excuse me, I
simply must go to the Executive Planning Meeting."

He got up, thinking he was free.

The Red Queen raised her voice. "If we're allocating time, Mr
Chairman, I'd like time for the Women's Peace Movement."

"Put it on the agenda, Miss Nash." John had almost got to the
door. The Red Queen stood up.

"I think we should have a meeting tomorrow."

"Saturday?" The White Rabbit looked alarmed.

"I want an international appeal. I'm going to get letters from women all over the world, and read them out."

"Who says you're going to? John returned to the table.

"I do."

John leant forward, his hands resting on the back of a chair, so that he was on a level with the Red Queen. "Mrs Snowden, you've not been put on this Board as a female tub thumper."

"Mr Chairman!" the Red Queen looked for help. "There is nothing more important than world peace, which we all agree is in danger once again. I'm sure none of us minds giving up a little of our precious time to discuss the subject. That is my motion. Will somebody second it?"

Nobody answered the challenge. Gainford looked at Carpendale hoping that he could avert the storm. John spoke deliberately. "Mr Chairman, I'm sure we've more than enough to do without having to sit and listen to a lot of the most utter balderdash."

"I'd like that put in the minutes." Mrs Snowden flashed a smile at Miss Stanley.

"All right," said John. "You know how to spell Balderdash, Miss Stanley. B A L . . . . ."

Mrs Snowden boiled over. "That remark is typical of the rudeness and discourtesy that I've had from you, Sir John, all day."

"I'm sorry. I've no wish to quarrel. But every meeting you come to you bring a fresh list of complaints a yard long."

'Well somebody has got to speak out about what goes on here."

"You know nothing about the B.B.C., and you know even less about me!"

"Just because I'm a woman!"

"Just because you're an interfering woman!" He sounded like John Knox addressing Mary Queen of Scots. "I'm ten minutes late for my next meeting, Mr Chairman, and I shan't get home till midnight." He turned back to Mrs Snowden. "As a woman, Mrs Snowden, you will appreciate that I am not only the Director General of the British Broadcasting Corporation, but I am also a married man whose wife is expecting a baby very shortly." This was news to all the members, who immediately relaxed into obligatory smiles. "So may I now leave this meeting?"

The White Rabbit cleared his throat. "You're going to be a father, eh?"

"I imagine so. Perhaps we can put that on the agenda as well?"

John left before there were any more reactions. The Red Queen was silenced, but not for long. Unfortunately Muriel couldn't produce a baby every other week!

Muriel sent for the nurse, but the baby showed a reluctance to do more than the occasional kick, and the nurse was sent home again, it being Whit Saturday. John walked round to the office and bumped into Peter, who said he'd tell Stella to go round and help Muriel to pass the time of day. John wondered what he was doing at Savoy Hill on Whit Saturday when there was only a skeleton staff. "I just dropped in to pick something up," said Peter. Later, John saw him getting into a taxi with some woman or other—not Stella—and looked forward to ribbing him about "picking something up"—a blonde, presumably.

After lunch, he took Muriel for a little walk in the park, and then they had tea. Muriel showed no signs of anything, so John went off and played tennis at Lady Arnot's till 6.45pm, when he hurried home to find there were still no symptoms. He stayed up late, not wanting to get into bed and the next minute be up again summoning the doctor. Eventually he went to bed, and didn't get up till 8.45 a.m., He looked out of the window and was surprised to see the doctor's car. He rushed in to see Muriel, and encountered the doctor who told him there was nothing to worry about, but Muriel had been having pains since 1 a.m..

"Why ever didn't you get me up?" John asked Muriel.

"I didn't see the point," she answered. "And I was quite right. The baby's still not come."

The pains persisted quite regularly, so John rang up the Odhams family doctor, Dr Sprott at Princess Risborough. He sensed that Muriel wasn't happy with the smart Westminster practitioner who was torn between making a little extra money and going off on his holiday.

It was already very hot, the sun beating down on the deserted London streets. John went up to Piccadilly and bought some medicine from the chemist. It made Muriel feel looked after, and gave John something to do.

He had breakfast at 11.30. Winnie didn't know what she was doing, serving toast and coffee at that hour. Dr Sprott arrived at noon and came down saying that Muriel would be all right with the nurse, and that she'd come back at night.

After lunch John went up to see Muriel and sat with her, reading to her from the biography of Nurse Edith Cavell, and then went and sat in the study trying to read. He kept the windows wide open, but it was still terribly hot, and he longed to get out and breathe the air. He thought of Muriel stuck upstairs and stayed where he was.

Later on in the evening, he suddenly heard groans. He went out into the hall, knowing the doctor hadn't come, and was very worried to hear the groans again. There was no sign of the nurse anywhere, so he went upstairs. The noise was quite loud and awful. On the landing he suddenly realised it was a cooing from the window. Opening it, he found a couple of pigeons. He peeped into Muriel's bedroom and saw that she was asleep, came back downstairs and sat for an hour in his study. He must have dropped off, for the next thing he knew he was wide awake, his whole body tingling. He'd had the old nightmare. He'd been out in No Man's Land alone, putting up a wire defence. Suddenly the darkness was lit up. A searchlight was scanning the perimeter, coming nearer and nearer till it focused on him, standing against the wire, his arms outstretched, clinging, waiting motionless for the burst of machine gun fire which would sweep across and finish him for good. He stood frozen . . . then he woke up. There'd been a thud in the room. he looked round at the open window, and saw a black cat staring at him. He got up and went over to it. The cat didn't move, and allowed itself to be picked up and stroked. John sat with it in his arms, stroking it and murmuring to it. He'd no idea where it came from. The cat seemed to like him. It was a good omen, so he kept it and called it "Timmy".

Dr Sprott came, and John felt left out of everything. His wife was having a baby, but it was nothing to do with him. She had a nurse with her and a doctor to give her chloroform. Yet the baby was his too. He sat in his chair in the study and went to sleep.

He was wakened by the nurse, shaking him.

"It's a boy, Sir John. Your wife would like to see you now."

He got up. It was as though Muriel had been part of the conspiracy. His son had been born and the nurse and doctor and Muriel had let him sleep through it. He picked a rose from the garden and took it with him.

Muriel was sitting up, looking quite bright and pleased with herself. John went over and kissed her. He didn't even glance at the baby which was in the cot beside her. She took the rose and held it to her face.

John said: "How are you, Musie?"

"Fine, I really am. Fine." Her voice was husky after the chloroform. "Have you seen your son?"

"Not yet." He tried to sound cheerful. He looked into the cot and saw a creased up tiny face, like a monkey. He thought it was astonishingly unprepossessing. He looked up from it, and saw faces all round, watching his reactions. Muriel was smiling.

"You can hold him, Lady Reith," said the nurse. She presented the baby to Muriel who held him in her arms. John saw them together—mother and son—Christopher and Muriel. Muriel looked radiantly happy and quite beautiful. He heard Winnie come in to join the chorus of admirers. He felt out of place. He'd suddenly remembered it was his mother's birthday too, and he hadn't sent her a card.

He went back to his study and closed the door. A feeling of utter depression had come seeping into his bloodstream, made worse by the knowledge that he should be happy. The music of Handel's *Messiah* increased the gloom, going round and round in his mind—"For unto us a son is born, unto us a son is given. . . For unto us a son is born, for unto us . . .!" He found the record and put it on the gramophone and felt worse. He went upstairs and had a hot bath and a good wallow. He was still there when the phone rang—the first enquiries and congratulations from Mrs Odhams. . . It went on like that for the rest of the day, so he forgot his depression, only for it to return twofold on Whit

Monday. He rang the office to tell them he wouldn't be coming
in and spoke to Betty Nash.

"You sound depressed, Sir John," she said.

"Do I? I ought not to be."

"No, you certainly ought not to be. What are you doing?"

"Reading. I shall probably draft the memorandum on television."

"What about tonight?"

"I'll stay put."

"Well . . . just a minute . . . " There was a long pause. "Sir John,
can Jo and I come round and see the baby this evening?"

"Yes, yes, of course." He felt suddenly cheered that Miss Nash
and Miss Stanley should want to give up their Whit Monday
evening for Muriel's sake.

He could hear laughter and chat in the office. "What's going
on, Miss Nash?"

It was Miss Stanley who answered. "My cousin Molly's here
and her boyfriend, and I've bought a car, Sir John—can we all
come round?"

"By all means. Come for tea."

"Thank you, that's lovely."

John put the *Messiah* on again, and it sounded wonderful. He
turned the volume up so that Muriel could hear it. Even the
constant stream of Muriel's family couldn't depress him, and by
the time Betty and Jo arrived with Molly and her boyfriend, he
was the "proud father" and did the honours with enthusiasm. He
even held the baby for a photograph by the boyfriend. He wasn't
sure why they'd come—was it curiosity?—had Miss Stanley
wanted to show him off like a giraffe in the zoo? They didn't care
about him really—why should they? They were like students
visiting their housemaster, as he used to visit his art master, Mr
Shaw at Greshams, and now Mr Shaw would come and visit him
at Savoy Hill and tell anecdotes about his behaviour in class.
He showed them Timmy and Jo stroked him.

"We must go, Sir John—we're going to Guildford. Would you
like to come with us?"

"Very much, but my duty is to remain at my post."

"Don't be silly. You can't do anything more—you've done

your bit. You'll only get depressed sitting with Timmy."

"All right. I'll just tell the nurse."

Miss Nash was surprised at Jo's boldness, and she was even more amazed to see the man she'd always assumed would never come down from the lofty heights and mix with ordinary mortals, shed the years and the responsibilities in the time it took him to put on his old tweed jacket and flannels.

They all crammed into Jo's new Austin and drove off to Molly's boyfriend's house. John, after a few early defeats, proved that his ping-pong days had not been wasted. Even the champion Molly lost a game to him. They danced to the gramophone, and Molly taught him the Charleston. She wasn't more than eighteen, with long black lashes.

"Are they false?" he asked. And she collapsed into giggles.

Jo and Betty dropped him back at the house. It was after midnight. He stood on the steps and watched the car out of sight, then he let himself in. The grandfather clock ticked loudly as he tiptoed upstairs to see if Muriel was awake. The light was on in her room, but she and the baby were fast asleep.

He came back down and made himself a blackcurrant drink, then sat in the study and wrote up his diary. "I played ping pong. I learned the Charleston. I was surprised I enjoyed it all so much. Molly said I should have learned years ago. I replied: 'I'm forty and I'll soon be dead'."

Jo Stanley got to the office first after the Whit weekend. She didn't want her boss to think that she'd take advantage of him after the previous night of ping-pong and dancing. She needn't have worried. When John bounded into the office with Peter Eckersley yards behind, he immediately said: "Last night was very jolly. You must ask Molly and her fiancè to come here for a return match! Let me have the plans for the new Headquarters will you please?"

He went into his office.

"Morning Miss Nash." She was sorting his mail. "I thought it extremely kind of you to include me in your party last night. We'll do the same again when the next baby comes."

Jo brought the plans and John spread them on the floor. He

wanted Peter to give his opinion on the studio accommodation. "Miss Stanley, I want to ask you a favour. These diaries of mine—I expect you've heard of them?"

"No, Sir John."

"Well I started them in 1911 and they're getting out of hand—*and* my scrap books. Would you like to take the job on?"

"What job, sir?"

"Type them out. I'll help you. I'll dictate. Miss Nash won't do it." He turned to Peter. "She says she doesn't want her morals corrupted!"

"Oh I don't mind about that," said Jo impulsively. Peter laughed. "I mean—I'm no good at typing. Last time I made an error, you sacked me!"

"Did I? Well you're still here, aren't you?" She joined in the laughter. "Think it over—there's no hurry—and give me your answer now."

"Don't bully her, John," said Peter.

"It's all right, I'll do it," said Jo.

"Good." John's tone was suddenly official. "Mind, this won't be done in B.B.C. time. It'll be extra-mural and paid for by me."

Jo went back to her desk, not knowing quite what she'd let herself in for. Miss Nash said nothing. She'd been shown bits of the diaries—Sir John had said there were at least a million and a half words and he ought to know—all written in an illegibly small hand. She didn't envy Jo.

"Don't put her off, Miss Nash." John read her thoughts. "She needs the money to keep her old mother."

"Yes, Sir John." Betty went out. He reminded her of a fussy old mother hen—she'd told him so more than once, when he'd come round to her flat at the end of the day, and sat warming his hands on a cup of cocoa, and mulling over the domestic problems of his staff and colleagues. She felt flattered that he should share his private opinions with her, but she sometimes felt that he treated her more like a stranger on the train than an intimate acquaintance. He told her once she was like his sister Beth. But apart from having the same name, she didn't see the connection. "I'm sure you'll have a good time, Jo," she said. "But he'll make you work."

20

John glanced through the mail—the usual massive pile. Churchill wanted to speak on India, while Ramsay MacDonald would be pleased to read the Bible during Lent. "Here's a pat on the back for you, Peter, from Buckingham Palace. His Majesty says will you please thank Captain Eckersley." He passed the letter over. "I told him the success of his broadcast was entirely due to your work—nothing to do with me."

"We got through to everywhere except Japan," said Peter modestly. "Can we talk about the studios later? I'll take the plans with me. Have you got a moment to spare?"

John decided there was only one word for Peter: "Glum". Most unusual. "What's the trouble?"

"Stella and I are parting."

"Who says so?"

"I do."

John sat down in his chair. Peter continued rolling up the plans. He seemed quite unconcerned as he replaced the rubber band. Then their eyes met. Peter was worried—the eyes were sad.

"What do you want me to do?" John asked.

"There's not much you can do, but I thought you ought to know. We managed to patch things up for a while, but now . . ." John was looking away from him, letting him see the stern wounded side of his face. "There's no going back, John."

"You want to get a divorce? That's definite?"

"Absolutely." Peter forced a smile. "A divorce absolute."

There was no answering smile from John. He remembered Peter and the blonde. He was going to rib him about it, but forgot. "Do I know her?"

"I don't think so."

"But she works here—on the staff?"

"Yes."

"Then I do know her." A statement of fact. "I'll tell you what I suggest you do. Take a couple of months grace leave—you're due for it. Does Stella know?"

"Yes."

"Then tell her you're going away to try and forget the girl. What about Switzerland? You could be at the World Association Conference some of the time. Charles'll be there to keep you company. They want to make him President—quite an honour." John cheered up and gave Peter a warm smile. . . with the other side of his face. "I suppose you love each other?"

"Yes. And we're very happy together."

"Well, see if you're happy apart. That's the real test."

When he got home, he told Muriel. She thought his advice very wise. "But what are you going to do if he comes back from Geneva and still wants to marry Miss Clark?"

"Miss Clark? So that's who it is. I might have guessed. How did you know she's the one?"

"Stella told me months ago."

"Why didn't you tell me?"

"She made me promise not to. I'm telling you now, John." She could see he was cross. "She told me as a friend. From what she said, I don't think there's any hope of Peter coming back to her. He's completely infatuated by Miss Clark. So what will you do?"

"I don't know. These damnable women, they don't mind what they do, or what misery they cause."

"From what Stella told me, it's Peter's fault."

"I'm not interested in Stella. Peter's done more for the B.B.C. than any other member of the staff. His name is better known in Europe than mine is. I don't want to see his name sullied and his career ruined."

"But why should it be ruined?"

John didn't answer. He went to his study and rang up Peter to find out whether he was going to take his grace leave or not. Peter said he'd talked it over with Stella and he'd go in the middle of the month. He sounded rather short, as though John had rung him up in the middle of the night.

John came back to Muriel. He watched her feeding Christopher. For the first time he seemed to notice him. The tiny fingers entwined themselves round his. He said: "I hope to God Peter sees sense."

John had stipulated exactly what he would require of the architect of the new Headquarters at Langham Place. Once these had been costed and agreed by the Board of Governors, he engaged the services of Sir Giles Gilbert Scott to oversee the building and let the Board get on with it, arguing that what was good enough for Liverpool Cathedral was good enough for the Board. He hoped that they would find sufficient to argue about in the building of the new Temple, not to worry him about the spiritual side. The Red Queen's insatiable appetite for discord, however, found no difficulty in swallowing the new Headquarters and still leaving plenty of room to digest endless memorandums and regurgitate the old disagreements. The questions of staff appointments and discipline, holidays and pay, unions, politics and peace movements were once more to be found on almost every agenda, and John began to dread the Governors' Meetings, particularly when the Admiral was not around to calm the atmosphere with his unsinkable good humour.

"Mr Chairman, I'd like to propose that the present motto of the B.B.C. be changed."

"What motto, Mrs Snowden?"

The White Rabbit appeared blandly curious, though John knew perfectly well that Mrs Snowden had already primed him with her questions.

"Quaecumque . . . and whatever the rest of that Latin is. 'Whatsoever things are honest and of good repute'."

"What do you suggest instead, Mrs Snowden?"

"I should prefer something much more up to date, such as 'Nation shall speak Peace unto Nation.'"

John had scarcely time to grunt disapproval before the motion was carried unanimously, and Mrs Snowden left the meeting hurriedly in order to consult directly with Gladstone Murray as to how to announce it to the waiting world.

John was so upset he developed indigestion, a rare affliction for him. He took three tablespoonfuls of syrup of figs, though Muriel begged him not to. Then he rang Ramsay MacDonald demanding that he remove "the silly Lord".

"Who do you mean, the silly Lord?"

"Lord Clarendon, the Chairman. He's a complete nincompoop, and he should never have been appointed."

"I can't sack him," said the Prime Minister.

"Well, offer him something else," said John.

The Prime Minister promised he'd do his best. He liked John and was glad to meet a fellow Scot halfway. Moreover, he had heard a good deal of what went on in the B.B.C. from next door at No 11 But he dared not risk offending Mrs Snowden while her husband was preparing his vital budget. He therefore did nothing. John was up all night.

By the time Carpendale returned from Geneva, John was so beside himself that the Admiral wanted him to see a doctor, but decided instead, to take him off to the theatre with Miss Nash and Miss Stanley. They had dinner afterwards, and spent the whole time running down members of the Board of Governors till John had quite recovered his equilibrium and was laughing at incidents which earlier on had reduced him to paroxysms of rage. He asked Carpendale all about the Radio Unions Conference.

"Burrows sent his warm regards, John. His only complaint about living in Geneva [Burrows was Secretary to the Union] was that there are no means of teaching his youngsters cricket. And he misses the English sea breezes, so he dopes them with iodine."

John laughed. "What about Eckersley? Did you see much of him?"

"Not really, he was . . . um . . . otherwise engaged."

"Oh?"

"He wasn't alone."

Both Miss Nash and Miss Stanley knew exactly who was being referred to, but the conversation was not pursued.

"Peter'll be back next week. I'm sure he'll come and tell you all about it," said the Admiral. "I tried my best," he added, "but I fear he's lost beyond redemption."

John made up his mind there and then what he'd do, what he *had* to do, the moment Peter got back from Geneva.

He asked to lunch with him at the Langham. He booked a table by the window, overlooking the new site. Mountains of earth were being removed, and the foundations were already going in. Peter was almost unable to eat his lunch, he was so fascinated by the scene.

"I met all manner of folk in Geneva. They were all asking about the new Tower of Babel. When will we move in?"

"The plan is for transmissions to commence in June, 1932. So that is when they will commence."

"I've got a lot of new ideas during my grace leave. I hope I'm not too late."

"That depends entirely on you."

They watched the workmen. Peter said: "I'm afraid your idea didn't work, John. We couldn't stay apart, we love each other too much."

"What about Stella?"

"She has accepted the situation."

As though changing the subject, John said. "I shall be sorry to leave the old place. I like the view from my window—the river, Lambeth Palace . . . I love it. Especially in the evenings—sunset. So many memories. I shall be sorry to leave it when the time comes. The new headquarters for me is a monster. I'm insisting an open fire in my office, otherwise they can do what they like."

The waiter asked them if they'd rather have their coffee at the table or in the lounge.

"We'll have it here, thank you," said John. They lit their cigarettes and smoked in silence. Peter knew John well enough to know not to interrupt the silences which punctuated his important conversations like deep pools in the rapids. "For you, Peter, that new Broadcasting House can be the culmination of your work—the most modern facilities, technical advances, your own inventions—it will be the Aladdin's Cave of your dreams. The start of a great adventure—voyage of discovery. . . It can only happen once in a lifetime."

The waiter poured their coffee, leaving the pot beside them. John didn't touch his. "You've been happy here, haven't you?"

"Yes very." He was being forced onto the defensive. "And I still am."

John put both elbows on the table and leaned his chin on his clasped hands. "Do you know a better, or more interesting, or more fulfilling job?"

Peter lowered his eyes. He knew already what John was trying to tell him. He wanted to get up and leave, before his life was uprooted.

"John, I know you have certain views on divorce, but . . ."

"I don't give two hoots about it. I mean that. I may be what the papers call 'a son of the Manse', but I believe that divorce is a matter which concerns two people."

Peter's sigh of relief was almost audible.

"Except where it concerns the B.B.C., and those of us who are privileged to lead. Bishops and Clergy, the Police, the Royal Family. . . and the B.B.C.. We must set an example. We cannot speak or act with authority if we transgress the laws."

"But I don't regard myself as leading people," Peter protested. "I'm not responsible for educating them or policing them. I'm not an artist. I just happen to be one of the few people in the world who really understands how radio and broadcasting works."

John leaned back in his chair, contemplating Peter like a schoolmaster searching for some means to communicate a simple rule of physics to a rather dull pupil. "Peter, you know that certificate that hangs behind my desk?"

"The one for regular attendance at Sunday School?"

"Is that what they say?" John smiled. "It testifies to my father's high distinction in his natural philosophy course at Aberdeen. He valued it almost more than anything he possessed. Because it was signed by the teacher for whom he had the most profound admiration—that great pioneer of wireless—Clerk Maxwell. And my father's photograph is on the other side of my desk. Both men are always at my elbow—Christian ethics and science. Those who believe in either and seek to advance their cause, must pay the price in full."

"I don't have your high ideals, John. I only know I love the job and I'll do it far better if I'm married to the woman I love."

John made no reply. Suddenly he tapped the table three times and said, "Shall we go?"

He stood up as the waiter hurried to pull back his chair, then walked resolutely to the door, holding it open so that Peter could go in front of him.

When they got to Piccadilly, John said, "I'm not going back to the office. I'm going home. I have to go to Birmingham next week. I'll see you when I get back. How soon do you want to leave?"

"Leave? You mean the B.B.C.?" John nodded. Peter was taken aback. "I . . . I haven't thought."

He was aware of the traffic passing him, someone buying an evening paper. He looked up at John. He was only a couple of inches shorter than John, but it was like looking at Nelson's Column. "I hadn't thought of going . . . I've no idea when I should. . ."

"Then I'll tell you. The sooner the better." He looked down at Peter. "Now."

They were standing in front of "Swan and Edgars", the meeting place of so many young couples. Peter'd met Stella there often. He felt as though John was not only telling him to leave the B.B.C., he was breaking all the ties of shared experience and friendship. But he took hold of John's hand with nothing but affection and gratitude. "O.K. John—now." He smiled. "I understand you."

"Do you Peter?

John let go of Peter's hand, but continued to look away from him, staring at the Guinness Clock opposite. He was no longer aware of the crowds circling Piccadilly Circus—perhaps it was the clock or the noise of the traffic, or the singing sensation in the ear where he'd been shot. He suddenly saw the gun carriage—the peaceful Flanders field, the hot sunshine, and Tudhope lashed to a wheel. John felt again the shock and horror of seeing the man he knew and liked suffering. The Adjutant had found him asleep on Guard Duty and sent him to a Field Court Martial. He was sentenced to Field Punishment No. 1. A week later John found him absent from his post—he was a hardened sinner, but a fine fellow and good with horses. John had him along to his billet and they talked together about home and people they both knew. After that there'd been no more crime. But the Adjutant was very angry when he heard about it and said John couldn't be a law unto himself . . .

Peter walked along Regent Street. He thought he might have a drink at the Regent Palace or the Cafe Royal. He wasn't sure where he was going. He only knew that he must go in the opposite direction to John.

At the next Board meeting, John explained Peter's departure. "I want to make it quite clear that he is resigning of his own volition. He'll go straight into another job with commercial radio advertising, and will receive a year's salary. It's a sad thing to have happened, but he knew the terms under which he was engaged originally, and his place will be taken by Noel Ashbridge."

There was a stunned silence. Even Mrs Snowden appeared confused. "Am I to take it that Captain Eckersley will no longer be attending the opening of the new London Station?" she asked.

"He will be there, and will receive the thanks of us all for his magnificent achievement."

There was more talk of farewell presentations and so on, but the meeting broke up with less than the usual acrimony. John hoped that the Governors had accepted the principle that divorce was not allowed among B.B.C. Staff.

Back in the office, Carpendale was not at all happy about it. "John, in future we must make changes. We can't risk a repetition of this sort of thing."

John agreed with him. "Yes, In future it will have to be put in the contract."

Carpendale stared at him. "You mean that future employees will have to sign a document promising not to fall in love with someone else if they're already married?"

"I mean that divorce is *verboten*, Charles."

"Have you spoken to Gladstone Murray about this?"

"No. Why should I?"

"The Press are bound to ask why Peter's leaving at the

moment of his greatest achievement."

"They're not bound to ask, and Murray's not bound to answer."

Carpendale went to see Murray and it was decided that as much as possible should be made of Peter's new job in advertising, and that any disagreements within the Corporation should be related to the well-known refusal of the Director General to countenance anything remotely to do with commercial broadcasting.

In the event, the opening of the Brookham's Park transmitter passed off without any sign of discord. Peter stood alongside John as though nothing had happened. He looked up at the heavy portico and remarked that he'd wanted to put a motto above it—"It is more blessed to send than to receive"—but could not think of the Latin. There was plenty of laughter and applause.

The next day John read the papers. He hadn't slept well, suffering from indigestion. He couldn't eat breakfast in any case, for the headlines made him feel sick. Peter's impending divorce was blazed across them, and the B.B.C. accused of sacking him for infidelity! Muriel advised John to stay at home if he didn't feel well, but he insisted on going to the office to prepare for the Board meeting that afternoon. Miss Nash was plainly upset by what she regarded as washing the B.B.C.'s dirty linen in public. John told Carpendale that he was going to scotch the business right away and rang Lord Clarendon. His Lordship's butler answered, asking if he could take a message, as his Lordship was in conference with the Governors of the B.B.C.. "No message," said John as he put the phone down.

For a moment or two he sat pondering on what action he should take. Then suddenly he recalled the butler saying, "His Lordship's in conference with the Governors of the B.B.C." In conference! It was 11.30 in the morning and there was a full Board meeting going on behind his back at the silly Lord's! He got up and paced about, then said to Miss Nash: "If anybody wants me I shall be over at Lord Clarendon's—in conference!"

"Do you want me to come with you, Sir John?"

"No. Just give me those newspapers." He strode out of the office, grasping his umbrella like a meat-axe.

By the time John got to Clarendon's house in Belgravia, his anger had ceased to seethe, but in its place was a determination to bring to an end the months of miserable frustration and turmoil which had beggared all his efforts. He knew all about the lunches which had become part of the Board's ritual before the meetings. He couldn't stop them having their secret pow-wows, but he was not prepared to allow Clarendon to hold meetings at his house and then roll up at the B.B.C. pretending that the Board Room was where the decisions were taken!

The butler answered the door. John brushed past him and walked into the drawing room. The White Rabbit, on his feet, and in the midst of some peroration, was dumbfounded to see the Director open the door and enter, but he immediately made him welcome, suggesting the butler take his hat and coat. John held out the newspapers for all to see. He needn't have bothered—copies festooned the room.

"Have you seen this?" he demanded.

"Yes, yes we have." Clarendon was unctuously polite. "As a matter of fact we were just talking about them. Would you like a cup of coffee, Sir John?"

"Discussing them—were you? In that case had you reached a decision as to how the B.B.C. should react to them?"

The Red Queen was undismayed. "I think they're, on the whole, very fair."

"Fair criticism," said Gainford.

"The *Daily Mail*?" It was John's turn to be dismayed. "You think that's fair?"

"The facts are all there," said Clarendon, gaining confidence.

"Facts—what facts?" John felt his anger returning. "Who said I sacked Peter Eckersley because he wanted a divorce?"

"I did," said Mrs Snowden boldly, flushing a menopausal pink. "But I never mentioned any names."

"Who else is the wireless genius of the B.B.C.?"

"I never called him that."

"And who else the tyrant?"

"I didn't call you that either."

"No, no, of course not." John held out the paper. "It only says in print that Mrs Snowden stated that anyone who crosses the path of this 'Mussolini of Broadcasting' suffers."

He flung the paper on the floor.

"Steady on," said Gainford.

"Mussolini!" John sat heavily. "Mussolini!"

Gainford glanced round at his colleagues, assuring himself that he had their full co-operation in trying to deal with a very unpleasant situation. "John, you know as well as I do the Press will make a story out of anything."

"I do indeed, and so does Mrs Snowden." He turned to her. "Who told you?"

"You did."

"Who told you all the rest of this?"

"I have my own methods—woman's methods, if you like . . ."

"You've been going behind my back. You admit it."

"Nonsense. You said yourself you would be very pleased if I would do something about the welfare of the staff. It's in the minutes. So that's all I've been doing. I've been meeting people, talking to them as human beings—learning from them what it's really like to be an employee of the B.B.C., with a dossier containing every detail about their religious beliefs and political opinions and their private life. Do you know, Lord Clarendon, there's a blacklist of employees who've offended against the code?"

"Don't talk rubbish, woman!" said John. "There's no blacklist— but if there was, you'd be on it!"

Mrs Snowden made an explosive noise, and Gainford intervened. "Now come on John, why shouldn't Mrs Snowden talk to the staff?"

"It's one thing to talk to the staff—but I will not countenance a member of the Board going round like the messing officer at dinnertime, asking the other ranks if there are 'any complaints'."

"Other ranks!" Mrs Snowden tossed her head.

"Yes, that's what they're called in the army. I'm not a pacifist, I don't know the jargon. I suppose you'd call them cannon fodder!"

"If you weren't the Director General, I'd slap your face!"

"As far as you're concerned I'm plain John Reith—so slap away!" He thrust his face down on a level with hers.

"Oh come on—really John," said Gainford with all the tolerance of an umpire upbraiding a prep-school boy.

"I'm sorry if this embarrasses you all." John looked round at the genteel group of committee men. "But it embarrasses me more than I can say to know that my own Board of Governors are in the habit of getting together in private . . ."

"Really!" Clarendon showed faint signs of temper. "It's quite unbearable. We can't even have a cup of coffee together without being spied on!"

"Don't be ridiculous . . ."

"How did you know we were here?"

"I rang up your butler to speak to you and he told me you were 'in conference'. Ask him! Do you think I've got a private detective following you about?"

The White Rabbit blinked at him. "In a word, yes. Yes, I do."

"And another in the B.B.C., reading your letters?"

"I' . . ." he hesitated. "I'm not saying that."

"Then why do you insist on having your letters sent on unopened?"

"I prefer to read them at leisure at home."

"Balderdash!" The cups almost rattled. "You are Chairman of the Governors of the British Broadcasting Corporation, and I am your Chief Executive, but what exists between us adds up to nothing but mistrust and secrecy. And in Mrs Snowden's case— downright treachery."

The Red Queen accepted the taunt gleefully. "Why not say treason? I'm guilty of High Treason and must be hauled in front of the Star Chamber and have my head chopped off!"

"You are guilty of using your privileged position on this Board and as wife of the Chancellor of the Exchequer, to defame me publicly through the newspapers."

"I'm trying to introduce a little democracy into . . ."

"You are trying to undermine the whole basis upon which the B.B.C. has been founded, and grown and flourished."

"Tyranny!" cried the Red Queen.

"Loyalty!" John ignored the Red Queen's mocking laughter. He went on with passionate conviction. "Each one of us loyal to the other. Every single person in the B.B.C. has direct access to me—from the lift boy to the chairman. If he's not happy with his lot, if he feels he's been badly done by—or if he has a personal problem—he knows I'll do everything in my power to put it right. And he knows that if he's got a dream, and I say "Yes", he'll have my unswerving loyalty and support against all-comers."

There was another silence. This time there was no embarrassment. If was impossible not to respect a man who kept such fine ideals in his head and wore his heart so plainly visible on his sleeve. Clarendon alone remained unimpressed. "I'll have your unswerving loyalty and support if you say 'Yes.' And if you say 'No', what then?"

John gave him a look of glacial disdain, and walked out.

21

There were those in Westminster who thought the Director General was going off his head. Certainly Mrs Snowden at No. 11 did nothing to dispel rumour and speculation. The Prime Minister appeared deaf to all voices, and John, having made one direct appeal to him earlier, could do nothing except put it about that he was looking for another job.

In reality, of course, he was quite determined to oust the White Rabbit, and was looking for another house. Muriel had never really taken to living in the heart of London. She hated the bleak and acid fogs, and longed for a garden and the country. There were no 'in-betweens' for John—he either lived in the middle of London or the Highlands, so he left it to Muriel to find a suitable rented house. She found Harrias House in Beaconsfield, but she had a hard job persuading John.

"Beaconsfield! That's twenty miles away!"

"Fifteen. It's lovely country and we'll be tenants of Lord Burnham and nice and near Doris and Peter and Uncle Willie and the Southams."

"The Southams? That's no recommendation." John thought Lord Southam, the managing director of Odhams Press, very opinionated. "He's either dogmatic or dull."

"Anyway, I've said we'll go and look at it."

"But I shall have to go backwards and forwards every day."

"Disraeli managed it. There's a very good railway service into Marylebone, and that'll be no distance from the new Broadcasting House. You'll be able to entertain people properly, and not have to rely on Roger Eckersley.

"Now don't you start nagging me about Thurloe Place!" His

public relations officer occupied a large house provided out of
B.B.C. funds to entertain important visitors. "The Red Queen's
got a bee in her bonnet on the subject."

"I'm not nagging, but Barton Street's too small. If you meet
people like Mrs Snowden away from London, they'd see you as
you really are, and maybe you'd see them differently."

"I don't want to see people like Mrs Snowden. God forbid!"

"Well then, you'd be able to get away from them!"

John laughed in spite of himself. "It belongs to Lord Burnham
does it?"

"Yes. I told him we were looking for somewhere, and he said
the house was vacant."

"Well I don't mind Lord Burnham, he was one of my
suggestions for Chairman, before Clarendon got his hands on it."
The mention of the silly Lord was enough to put him off the
house again. "No, no, I want somewhere near the sea."

"But John it's ideal. It's got ten acres and Christopher can keep
a pony. Look, Lord Burnham gave me a photograph." She
produced it. "It's rather enormous, I'm afraid."

John seemed to quite like it. "Looks Edwardian."

"Some of it is."

"Well, if it's really enormous, I don't mind. I don't want to
exchange the hub of the universe for a country cottage. We'll go
over and see it this afternoon."

John never wasted time. He liked the house and decided to
keep hens.

He was telling Miss Nash all about it, waxing quite lyrical. "I've
always liked hens. They render selfless service, and when their
egg laying days are over, they make the supreme sacrifice in a
good white sauce!" Miss Nash and Miss Stanley laughed, and the
phone rang. John picked it up. "Reith."

It was Gladstone Murray. "Sir John, I've got some news for
you that may be of interest."

"Go ahead." John wasn't sure about Murray ever since the
Eckersley business. He felt he should have kept the Press at bay.

Murray was bubbling over with excitement. "Well, I've just
been talking to a friend of mine in Capetown, and he says—wait
for it—the Governor Generalship has been offered to Clarendon

and he's accepted it!"

"You're sure?"

"Certain. My friend's Editor of News Agencies out there."

John heard Miss Nash gasp. She was listening on the parallel. "Thank you, Bill. That's the best news I've had since the Armistice."

He jumped up and gave Miss Nash a hug. "What do you think of that, Miss Nash? What can we do to celebrate. We must do something. Ring out the old, ring in the new!" he recited and did a dance, and then rang Carpendale in Brussels and told him the glad tidings in French.

Muriel came in at five and John broke the news to her. "I can't wait to see the silly Lord's face when he gets back from Switzerland. My prayers are answered—not quite in the way I had imagined though. Yesterday I prayed fervently that he'd fall off his skis and break his silly neck. I thought at the time it was too much to hope for, but God moves in a mysterious way!"

Lord Clarendon's term of office had still seven months to run, and he continued to obstruct, delaying John's salary increase which had been agreed at £7,500 months before. John complained to Ramsay MacDonald, and could hardly contain his delight when the White Rabbit was informed by Downing Street that he had to relinquish the Chairmanship immediately so that John Whitley could take over.

Whitley was the former Speaker of the House of Commons, an elder statesman of long experience. Like everybody else, he'd heard rumours of what had been going on between Sir John and the Board of Governors. He knew Mrs Snowden personally, and Lord Clarendon by repute. Lady Astor was one of those who defended the Director General when asked. "It's the clash of opposites," she told him. "Sir John is a born leader, a brilliant organiser, a man with ideals and ideas. Clarendon is the stupidest man I've ever met. If he even had an idea in his head he couldn't keep it there long enough to absorb it."

John decided that he was lumbered with a different version of the same thing. Whitley might not be obstructive, but he was old and as ignorant of broadcasting as his predecessor. Moreover, it was his committee which had produced the report on pay and conditions throughout the Civil Service. John naturally supposed that the new Chairman would try to implement similar reforms within the B.B.C. The mistrust he felt for Clarendon was transferred to John Whitley. He'd wanted Lord Burnham for Chairman or better still—himself.

But John Whitley was no ex-Etonian aristocrat. He was a Yorkshireman, accustomed to dealing with ambitious politicians and furthering their aims. He saw at once a man in the mould of Lloyd George or Winston Churchill, who knew what he wanted and was determined to get it. Whitley was at the end of his career, facing the inevitable anti-climax of retirement and as John expounded his views on broadcasting his ageing imagination was fired again. Instead of becoming a government tool, he threw in his lot with John and became his guide, philosopher and loyal friend.

"I want you to know, right from the start," he said, "that I regard the position of Chairman as complementary to Director General. You're the man with the ideas, and my job is to see they're not wasted."

John's response was to take Whitley completely into his confidence, and together they planned and executed the next big step forward for the B.B.C.—the opening of the new head-quarters.

Two chairs and a table were all that remained in number 6, Barton Street. John took his last meal there, and watched the removal men clear away the last wee sticks of furniture. He closed the door on a period of his life which had taken him from virtual bachelordom to marriage and fatherhood, from Scottish obscurity to fame and fortune.

He moved to Harrias House and immediately suggested to Lord Burnham that he change the name. His Lordship refused, but was quite happy to allow John to alter the house as he pleased. Central heating was installed and French windows. There were now four servants, but even so the house was full of empty rooms waiting to be furnished by Muriel and occupied by visiting relatives, who appeared on all sides staying for weeks on end. John was only too glad to welcome Doris and her new

husband, Peter, to whom promptly offered a job. He was pained
when it was refused. A similar offer, however, to Muriel's
brother Lynch, was eagerly accepted. Lynch, like Muriel was shy
and retiring. Still John was determined not to show favouritism.
He could start on the editorial staff of *Wireless World*—at the
bottom. Robert received no such preferential treatment, particularly as he only came to see John to ask him to give evidence in
Edinburgh in his divorce case. John was prepared to write out a
statement to the effect that Robert hadn't lived with his wife
since 1926, but he had no intention of going up to Edinburgh
and appearing in court. It seemed to be Jean all over again,
except that Robert wasn't going to the House of Lords. John felt
quite sorry for him, in fact, as he was obviously still in love and
couldn't even bring himself to mention the "other man". He
wrote a cheque for £100, and wondered why he was supposed
to support his entire family.

John decided to give up smoking for Lent. He told Muriel he
was making a small sacrifice to God as thanks for recent mercies.
He listed other reasons and stuck them on his dressing table: 1)
Christian principles; 2) Discipline; 3) Mental and physical
benefit; 4) Uxorial amenability. Muriel found him very irritable
and looked forward to Easter—not that she expected to see
much of John during the holiday. He was more busy than ever at
the B.B.C. Mrs Snowden's "Women's Peace Movement" had
received a momentary setback, but in its place came a delegation
of Welsh children. John thought the whole thing absurd and
ridiculous, and said so. The children said he was as bad as a
Welsh coal owner. It was hardly to be expected that a man who
only liked children in very small doses and closely identified the
cause of peace with his arch-enemy, the Red Queen, would alter
his policy of strict impartiality in all matters which concerned the
B.B.C.

Yet although he was aware of the undercurrents which were
so soon to suck Europe under—hence his dislike of being called
Mussolini—he accepted the invitation of the German Deutch-
rundfunk to attend some inauguration celebrations, without any
thought of political implications. He spoke German and his
reception in Berlin left him in no doubt as to the high esteem in

which he was held. The Germans, like most other countries, had
sought the guidance of the B.B.C. when establishing their
wireless networks, and welcomed him as the Martin Luther of
broadcasting. At the Opera, he stood up in the Royal Box and
received a royal ovation. It was the start of an important official
visit which developed into a delightful holiday in Bavaria as the
guest of Dr Wanner and his family.

John's total lack of protocol and English stuffiness at once
made him one of the family. Moreover, the Wanners had three
attractive daughters, Beth, Irene, and Ina who took him swimming on the lake and made a great fuss of him. He liked them all,
but eventually settled for Irene, aged sixteen, as his favourite. He
wondered what Muriel would say if she suddenly appeared and
found him sunbathing on a raft with a beautiful German maiden
rubbing sunburn lotion over his back! Besides this there were
visits to museums and churches and an atmosphere of respect
and admiration which was balm to his sore mind. The prophet
might not be honoured in his own country, but in pre-war
Germany the name of John Reith stood for the freedom and
honour and civilisation which was just beginning to flower in the
Republic, only to be ruthlessly crushed a year or two later. John's
relationship with Germany was not founded on vague inter-
nationalism. He loved Bavaria as he loved Scotland and he made
the Wanner family his own.

He returned to London, refreshed and resolved never again to
allow his judgments to be warped and his progress impeded by
senseless incompetents. The next two years would see the
opening of the new headquarters, and the emergence of the
B.B.C. as visibly the most important and potent force for good
throughout the world. Unlike the American wireless networks,
the words would not be diluted by advertisers and civil servants.
Five years earlier, at the time of the General Strike, John had said
to Churchill that the voice the world would hear would be the
voice of the B.B.C.. From now on that voice would be unique and
personal, it would be the voice of one man—John Reith. The
spirit of benevolent dictatorship was abroad in the land.

The move from Savoy Hill provided John with an ideal

opportunity to enjoy one of his favourite pastimes—throwing out. He'd done a fair amount when they moved from Barton Street, but they needed most of the furniture, and Muriel had stacked odds and ends not immediately required in the spacious outhouses and stables at Harrias. The new Broadcasting House had no such store places, and old letters and impedimenta couldn't be preserved forever. So Miss Stanley and Miss Nash sorted through the files and John kept interesting items for his scrapbooks. Possessions meant nothing to him unless they had associations with important events or people he respected or loved. Memories were what he treasured and sought to preserve —one of the reasons he kept his diaries. And yet he found it a very unsatisfactory and disappointing way of reliving the past to have to plough through hundreds of pages in order to find what he'd given Musie for Christmas ten years before, or what she'd given him. He therefore decided to organise his diaries at the same time as Miss Stanley typed them out.

Like everything else John did, it was done with care and thought and with little consideration for Jo's feelings, as she was forced to type out uncomplimentary remarks about herself. In the early days John had regarded her as irritating and not very efficient, and it was all faithfully recorded. John, reading the finished product over, saw a pattern of life unfolding before him, which seemed to be repeating itself without any hope of novelty. There were lunches and dinners, meetings of the advisory committees, and encounters with almost every rich and famous visitor to London.

He glanced through 1930. He seemed to have done nothing in January but read *The Good Companions* and the *Testament of Youth* and go to the theatre. February he'd met Jezebel and her wretched mother in Westminster Chapel. He'd had to be polite because his mother was with him to try out the new hearing phones. And as for March . . . All he had done about the move from Barton Street to Beaconsfield, was put up the pictures in the new house and walk around the garden, and go to the local church which was "terrible!"

Never mind, after all his diary was also a valuable account of the politics of the day. He turned the page—So Beaverbrook wanted to be Prime Minister? He'd forgotten that. It seemed everyone was after Ramsay MacDonald's job. Not surprising really—a nice enough fellow, but weak. Fancy appointing Whitley like that, without any consultation and without doing anything about his own position at the B.B.C. It was pure chance that Whitley had turned out to be just the man for the job—pure chance that they'd liked each other. Pure chance . . .

That was another aspect of the diary—the extent to which a man's life was affected by chance. Was it only chance that had made him go to the Memorial Chapel on November 10th and turn up the pages of the Cameronians to find Wallace's name? Wallace, the corporal who'd been his constant companion and friend—they'd gone riding together, which had angered the Adjutant. He'd found Wallace's name, and the day on which he was killed was November 10th. Was that pure chance to be killed the day before Armistice, and for John to go to the Memorial Chapel and remember him?

He felt suddenly overwhelmingly sad. Wallace was dead and John Reith was alive, and the year had gone past him with nothing to show for it but being elected Deputy Chairman of the Athenaeum and buying a "jolly new henhouse on wheels".

He could hear Mrs Snowden ranting on at the Appeals Committee. Her voice alone was enough to set his teeth on edge. He got up. "I'm going over to the Savoy, Miss Nash."

"Don't forget Charlie Chaplin's coming to tea, Sir John."

He hadn't forgotten. Miss Nash irritated him too with her endless reminders. He wanted to meet Chaplin more than anyone—more than the King of Spain or Einstein, or Paderewski. What an extraordinary commentary on modern civilisation! He wondered what he'd put about him in his diary. Nothing, he supposed. What could Charlie Chaplin say that would be the least memorable?

He walked down the passage and past the Board Room. Mrs Snowden was complaining about there being no private lavatories in the new building. Whatever had that got to do with Parry's dismissal? What was there about that woman that made him dislike her so? He got into the lift and Kilroy didn't speak. He saw him every day—there was a tacit agreement between the two men that they didn't have to chat aimlessly. And yet he was getting on better with Mrs Snowden than at any time. Whitley was a marvellous oil on troubled waters. Mrs Snowden, of course, wanted another term of office—over his dead body! At their last Board Meeting she'd told him all about Philip Snowden's illness. He felt almost sorry for her, but much more sorry for her husband.

He entered the Savoy and sat down in his usual place. The usual waiter took his usual order. Fish was a safe one. He was sure he was getting, or had got, an ulcer. He wasn't looking forward to his forthcoming visit to the land of enormous steaks and pumpkin pie. But he was going to take Muriel with him to the U.S.A. and it would be fun to introduce her to his old friends. He was giving her a dog for her birthday. He hoped it would have time to settle in before they went. To be on the safe side, he'd give her two. She wanted a red setter, but he preferred a cairn.

On April Fool's Day he got the £7,500 at last. He still almost didn't accept it. He complained to Muriel. "For once the Red Queen spoke up for me. She said she'd back me for Chairman when the new Charter comes up, but as I didn't say I'd back her for another term, £7,500 was carried unanimously with no back payments. They are incredibly mean—even Whitley!"

"Never mind," said Muriel. "We're quite well off, and my Odhams shares are booming." She was quite happy with C.J. her son, at Beaconsfield. John wanted a daughter to go with him.

"Any sign of Diana yet?" He liked the name, and was trying to get Muriel used to it.

"Not yet. I'll tell you the moment there is," said Muriel. She too wanted a daughter, but not one called Diana. "And let's not decide on a name until the baby's born." Meanwhile the red setter was proving to be hopelessly nervous, so John returned it and called the little cairn "Rufus".

Muriel and John sailed to New York on the *Aquatania*. Muriel was a good sailor who thoroughly enjoyed the trip as a normal passenger. John never relaxed for a moment, insisting on examining the ship from stem to stern. "I've always wanted to command a battleship," he informed his wife. "I think I'll take navigation when we get home, and join the R.N.V.R." He was also curious to know more of the principles of ventilation so that they might be applied to the new Broadcasting House.

"Get that launched first" was Muriel's advice.

Once John had got Muriel through the Customs—he was allowed ashore as a distinguished visitor without any baggage check, but that didn't include his wife—he made a triumphal progress to the White House to meet President Hoover. He noted the President's habit of staring fixedly at the bottom button of a visitor's waistcoat and agreed with Democrat friends that "The President is despicable, and running the country at two-guinea pig power!"

But the highlight of their visit was John's return to the place which had been home to him during the war. The old pastor greeted him like a son. The warmth of friendship and understanding once again surrounded him. He read the lesson in the new church which had cost two million dollars—admired and was admired. Muriel stayed in the background as always. Swarthmore was the essence of Pennsylvania—Presbyterian and Quaker. John had often told her about it. He'd even suggested that they emigrate during that dreary out-of-work period in the early days of marriage. She could just see him as an American citizen, challenging the world. It would have suited him down to the ground. But she longed to get back to Beaconsfield. The constant company of John was overpowering—like the Rockies which they also visited before returning. John let her read his diary at the end of it all. During the five weeks they were away there had not been one day on which they were not either socialising or rubber-necking or travelling. But she enjoyed herself. They hadn't been so close since the Brighton days—so relaxed and unworried. Somewhere on the voyage home she'd started a baby. Diana was a fact.

22

One of the reasons why John found the Board more amenable than of yore was the "monstrous white elephant" now nearing completion. They could all find some practical way in which their personalities could be expressed. The artists among them could attack or defend Eric Gill's nude Ariel over the entrance, the scholars argue about the dedication in the hall, the financiers add up and subtract. Rendell, as headmaster of Winchester, was given the task of providing a suitable inscription in Latin. John's only stipulation was that they should go back to his original motto from the Bible, "Whatsoever things are honest and of good repute . . .", and do away with Mrs Snowden's "Nation shall speak peace unto nation". He didn't approve of having his own name recorded as the First Director General, but appreciated the wholehearted spirit of Whitley's insistence.

They went together one day to visit their new offices. John looked round his room with distaste. True, they had put in a fireplace, but he hated the shape of the windows. The size of it was reasonable for someone who liked to walk up and down. He'd decided to put in a wardrobe too, so that he wouldn't have to go home every time he put on his obligatory dinner jacket. There didn't seem to be any suitable corners—people were right who said the building looked like a battleship. And the walls were so bare. Whitley agreed with him.

"You can't imagine anyone sitting in here having a chat and a smoke," he said.

"It wants panelling," said John. "Your office too."

"Why not panel the whole lot?"

"Yes. That'll make all the difference," John said hopefully, knowing in his heart that it wasn't merely the feeling of his office which was wrong, it was the feeling of the whole building. There was nothing "cosy" about it. It was all so functional, and what irritated him to excruciation was the certainty that even in that respect it was found lacking. The concert hall was inadequate. What was the point of commissioning William Walton to compose a new work when there wasn't room on the platform for the musicians? And when they tested the acoustics, the sound came out through the ventilating shafts and drowned the studios! He much preferred the old warehouse at Savoy Hill. For once he was in total agreement with the Red Queen, now promoted to Viscountess after her husband's resignation and preferment to the Lords. He'd made a point of ringing her up on the day it was announced, and surprising her with "Good morning, your ladyship." There was also the decor, and the canteen buried in the bowels of the earth. John liked to eat with "the men" sometimes. Nor did he like the way in which his office appeared to be insulated from the work which was at the heart of the building. The chapel was conveniently placed, but when he emerged from his inner sanctum he felt as though he were coming out from the vestry into an empty church. Whitley tried to reassure him.

"I'm sure you'll soon stamp your personality throughout the building, John. Give yourself time."

"I shall be sad to leave Savoy Hill. I doubt if I shall ever feel the same towards Broadcasting House."

If he felt like that about it, he was sure many others would, and he determined to forestall any rumblings of regrets from the very beginning. It was now April, and in a couple of months the building would be occupied. "We must plan the opening ceremony very carefully," he said to the Chairman. "We must make everyone feel that this is the continuation of a great endeavour—not the start and not the finish." He was talking to himself. He knew that the opening of Broadcasting House was the end of an era.

John refused Whitley's offer of supper. He wanted to get home in good time. "Muriel's due at any moment, and she's taken to going to bed early." He rather liked going to the Whitleys' house in Westminster. It reminded him of Barton Street, which he still hankered after. He didn't much care for commuting, and was becoming bored stiff by the "regulars" who tried to inveigle him into conversation about the B.B.C. There was one neighbour in particular—a barrister—who had driven him to take refuge in the guard's van on more than one occasion. His speciality was divorce, which John found a depressing subject at the best of times. Robert was miserable. He missed the children and yet refused to do anything about custody of them. When Jean and he were together he left the room and let them exchange their unhappy experiences.

He took Muriel for a little walk in the garden before it got dark. Clark, the gardener, had prepared a level spot for the new summer house which he'd ordered from Harrods. They discussed household arrangements for the arrival of the baby. Christopher's nursemaid had not proved much use, and Muriel had given her notice a couple of days earlier. John liked the girl and felt sorry for her. She was only eighteen and would have to go back to living with her mother. He said he'd have a word with her, and after dinner he went up to the nursery where she was listening to the news. He'd only been there a few minutes when Winnie came in, very fussed because the bedroom door was locked from the inside and Muriel was on the phone in the study. John hurried downstairs and tried the door for himself. It was locked, as was the dressing room. He knew immediately what was wrong. The police had warned him a month ago that there had been a number of robberies in the district—Lord Burnham for one had been burgled the previous year. He told Winnie to fetch Clark and went down to the study to phone the police and break the news as gently as he could to Muriel.

"You're not to worry, Musie, but we've just been robbed, and there's a fair chance the burglar's still in the house. Give me the phone I've got to ring the police."

Muriel rang off without explanation to her sister. John was organising a plan of attack as though the bedroom was an enemy machine-gun post.

"Get as many men up here as you can," he told the constable at the other end. "I'll make sure they don't escape."

The policeman didn't seem to understand at all. How did he know there had been a robbery if he hadn't been in to the bedroom?

"He's come in through the window, same as the fellow did who kidnapped the Lindbergh baby!" That stirred the constable up. It also worried Muriel.

"Is Christopher all right?"

"Oh yes, your ladyship," Winnie assured her. "I went to his bedroom first."

She'd brought Clark over. They'd passed a ladder in the bushes. John went outside to investigate. He could see the bedroom window was open. Obviously the burglar had gone. He grabbed an axe to break the door down, just as the police force arrived—one elderly constable on his bike.

The three of them went back upstairs and managed to prise the dressing room door open. Muriel wouldn't stay downstairs and came into the bedroom as soon as John unlocked the door. Things were all over the floor but there was no damage to the furniture. John went straight to the bedside commode which housed the chamber pot and his service revolver. Both were intact.

"John!" Muriel was searching a drawer in her dressing table. "They've taken all my jewellery."

"Are you sure? How do you know?"

"I tidied it all away—put it in my jewel case, so as to have everything tidy for the birth." She was in tears. John looked in his dressing room. His father's gold watch was gone, and a few odds and ends of no great intrinsic value. But there were irreplacable mementoes which were missing, and Muriel had lost everything except her wedding ring and gold wrist-watch. "My engagement ring, John!" She was very upset. She picked up his revolver for the first time—she'd always refused to touch it in the past. "If they were here now I think I'd shoot them."

John tried to comfort her. "Luckily they've not found your fur coats." They were still in a drawer. Musie went over to the cot that she'd so lovingly prepared. It had been left alone, with the baby things in the basket beside it.

Then the inspector arrived and phoned up the stations at

2.   *Reith at the Races*

13.   *Reith with the B.B.C. Staff*

14.   *Reith with his mother and children, Marista and Christopher*

15   From the B.B.C. dramatisation—Reith (Tom Fleming) confronts Mrs Snowden (Mona
      Bruce): "It was like 'Alice in Wonderland'. I called Mrs Snowden the Red Queen and Lord
      Clarendon the White Rabbit." (B.B.C. Enterprises)

16.   Vice-Admiral Carpendale (James Grout) reads extracts from the **Daily Mail** to Reith
      (Tom Fleming) in the B.B.C dramatisation: "The B.B.C., under the guidance of Sir John
      Reith, is the nearest thing in this country to government by the Nazis." (B.B.C. Enterprises)

17. From the B.B.C. dramatisation, Reith (Tom Fleming) answers his critics on the select committee: "This is one of the rare occasions when I'm going to permit my terrorised staff to speak for themselves." (B.B.C. Enterprises)

18. A sample from Reith's diaries

Marlow and High Wycombe. But it was clear that the birds had had plenty of time to fly back to London. Nevertheless, full details were taken down. They didn't get to bed till two in the morning, having to sleep in their room without being allowed to clear up.

Next day it was all over the papers, and John couldn't resist feeling a kind of pleasure that the Director General of the B.B.C. could command so much attention from the Press.

The police investigations, which involved lists of goods lost and taking fingerprints and all the rest of the legal process, kept John away from the office for the weekend. But on Sunday night Jo Stanley came over to see them and he dictated a long letter of complaint to the Chief Constable. The uncomplaining Jo had to call in at the B.B.C. on her way home to type it out. The Chief Constable responded in a suitably contrite manner and promised to do all he could to help by providing a policeman on duty till 4 a.m. He also accepted an invitation to dinner. He was called Warren and had been a Colonel in the Army Service Corps, so John didn't expect he'd be up to much. Muriel still felt uneasy at night, and with the Lindbergh scare so recent, John took on a nightwatchman. He felt it was really a bit unnecessary, but for Muriel's peace of mind Peg Leg Pete and his dog patrolled the grounds all night long. Lord Burnham agreed to go shares in a new six-foot high fence all round. Burrows—who came over for the opening of Broadcasting House—reported back to his former colleagues that all night long he was kept awake by the night watchman making his rounds, tap-tapping like Blind Pugh in *Treasure Island.* Others with less sense of humour latched onto it as yet another example of the Director General's delusions of grandeur and paranoia. Nobody appreciated just how much John felt the loss of the sentimentally precious things. He didn't like to admit that Charlie's cuff links had meant anything to him. John thought of writing to him and wondered how Charlie would react if he knew what he thought of him now! He went to his study and took a bundle of Charlie's letters from a drawer. He and Christopher burned them on a bonfire.

The baby was now overdue, but Dr Milligan assured John that

the shock of the burglary would not have affected the baby and
that he needn't worry.

He returned to work, only to find the Red Queen waiting for
him to discuss the everlasting Opera troubles. He asked her to
wait till he'd had a chance to speak with the Postmaster General
who was hinting that he might suspend the grant for the present
financial year—at least so Murray had told him.

John took Murray with him to see the Postmaster General,
who confirmed he might indeed suspend the grant.

"That'd be a most dishonourable thing to do, sir," said John.

"Not if I was acting with the direct authority of the House of
Commons."

"I don't agree, sir. Even with the vote of the House, it's a
dishonourable action." The feeble little creature was trying to
foist the blame on to the back benchers.

"Sir John, a great many people are very concerned about the
constitution of the B.B.C. and the internal administration. It's
being said quite openly that there should be some form of
enquiry."

"You've been reading the *Daily Herald*, sir. Surely you're not
influenced by that!"

"Sir John, you mustn't forget that most of the programmes you
present are in fact subject to my personal approval. I have
to stand up in the House of Commons—you don't."

Politics, thought John, that's all it is—politics. He hardly
listened to the rest of the argument about how the B.B.C. should
give the public what it wanted, and that Whitley had no
experience of broadcasting . . . John remembered he'd got an
Athenaeum meeting at 4 o'clock at which Whitley was to be
nominated for membership, and excused himself hurriedly.
Murray stayed behind with the P.M.G.

John thought nothing of it at the time, but in the train going
home, he wondered whether perhaps there was more to
Gladstone Murray than he'd realised. That there were traitors in
the camp who sided with the Government busybodies he knew
very well—but mostly they were down at the bottom of the
heap. Gladstone Murray was one of his trusty lieutenants and
Mrs Snowden had even suggested him for Deputy Director

General when Carpendale eventually retired . . . Was he another rat gnawing at the foundations? It was a sickening thought, and it wouldn't go away.

He was glad to get home and find everything in order. The nurse suggested he rang Dr Barbara Sprott, as Muriel had at last shown signs of an imminent delivery. Dr Sprott said she'd come over at 10 p.m. and he phoned Whitley to tell him about the interview with the P.M.G. and congratulate him on his unanimous admission to the Athenaeum. Then he set about moving furniture around in the bedrooms, as in addition to accommodating the nurse there would be Drs Milligan and Sprott, plus Mrs Shirley—Muriel's aunt. By 11 o'clock Muriel was still lying peacefully in bed, while down below in the study they were having quite a party, playing Kum Bak, during which John asked if the doctors and nurses were being paid for the job or by time! Then the Orpheus Choir came on the wireless, and John turned it up very loud, and stood at the bottom of the stairs and sang with them for Muriel and the baby—Psalm 124. He went upstairs to see Muriel, and there were tears in her eyes.

At five to seven he woke up to find Dr Milligan standing by his bed. He looked so grave that John thought something terrible had happened to Muriel and the baby. Then the doctor said, "You've got a fine daughter."

John went in immediately to see Muriel. She was completely exhausted, having been in labour all night. The baby weighed 11½ lbs. Unlike Christopher, the new born baby looked beautiful to John.

23

When the B.B.C. flag fluttered for the first time from the masthead above Broadcasting House, he behaved like a general after a great victory and as acclaimed as such. He acknowledged his achievement, but made it clear that, like Shakespeare's *Henry V*, the glory belonged to God, and he wasn't interested in any honour less than a baronetcy. When he looked round at the distinguished men and women who attended the gala dinner to celebrate the B.B.C.'s coming of age, he considered that he'd never seen such a miserable crowd with their ill-gotten medals and sashes. "None of them's done a quarter of what I've done," he whispered to Muriel. Nevertheless he accepted the lavish compliments that they poured over him like sweet-smelling oil.

"None of the great figures of the past, like Gladstone, has done more good," said Ramsay MacDonald. "This country and the whole world is under a debt of gratitude!" He agreed with the Prime Minister's words wholeheartedly, but not with what followed from Whitley. "You deserve to be the proudest and happiest man in the world, Sir John, and I thank you from the bottom of my heart." How could he be proud and happy when the words of the old prayer were uppermost in his mind—"We have done those things we ought not to have done, and left undone those things we ought to have done"?

But when he had earlier on addressed his whole staff in the new Concert Hall, he'd had no such inhibitions. "I am proud and I am happy today because I feel I am surrounded by my friends. Mind you, I've heard it said that we're such a vast organisation we're rather lacking in soul, so I prefer to use the word 'organism'—a collection of individuals working together to produce programmes, each dependent on each other."

The Board applauded politely, but John wasn't talking about them, he was talking about the loyal friends who had started with him when the B.B.C. was only three or four people and a microphone. "Now amongst this organism, I'm glad to see one or two individuals who preceded even my own coming! Step forward Mrs Bottle, and Kilroy and Plater!" The telephonist and the two doormen came to the front amidst laughter and applause. "Behold the three remaining aboriginals!"

Muriel wondered at the mastery John had of people and events and his unfailing ability to entertain an audience the moment he got to his feet.

"We've got eighteen survivors from the original thirty-one who came with me to Savoy Hill. I'm glad of your moral support in the front row."

He continued to recall the early days with light-hearted enthusiasm, but Muriel was seated beside Roger Eckersley, and he didn't smile. There were others too who wore a mask, like Gladstone Murray who smiled fixedly as befitted the Public Relations Officer. Perhaps he was thinking of the people who didn't survive—a hundred and fifty-seven of them had left the B.B.C. in five years for one reason or another. Not merely those failing to make it in the ordinary rough and tumble of a competitive world, but men like Peter Eckersley and Burrows— gone elsewhere because they didn't fit into the system—the system preserved in likeness of its creator, John Reith.

John's manner became serious. "Now some of you may miss the old place. Don't. I have an affection for it as the scene of great labour and some achievement for those who worked there with me in the past. But I do not regret what is past, because regretting the past is a great mistake. I look forward and nothing but forward to the future."

The official opening of November 10th to commemorate the anniversary of the founding of the British Broadcasting Company exactly ten years earlier was a much more sober occasion. Not that alcohol was ever served officially at any B.B.C. gathering— even for medicinal purposes: the Langham Hotel, like the Savoy before it, was the unofficial club.

His Majesty King George V and Queen Mary had been invited to perform the ceremony with a golden key. Unfortunately, the whole Board wished to escort them round the new building. John insisted that he would play host to the King, and Sir Charles Carpendale—knighted on June 7th—should do the same to the Queen. There was a good deal of ill feeling among the Board, particularly from Lord Gainford. But John was determined that their Majesties should enjoy themselves. He'd been a fairly frequent visitor to Windsor Castle, where he usually managed to provide a welcome relief from the stuffiness of court occasions. His eccentricities of behaviour and conversation enlivened the evening without ever impinging on royal protocol. And John, who would have been bored stiff on other occasions, suffered gladly for the sake of his sovereign. He was a profound monarchist at a time when the thrones of Europe were crumbling on all sides. He even held rehearsals of the National Anthem, so that the King could hear it sung as he wished. He announced "Our most distinguished listener is very insistent of getting the emphasis right on the last line Not *God save the King*, but *God save* the *king*! Now all together!" and the B.B.C. concert hall echoed to the rendition of the anthem.

Though they joined in with apparent patriotic fervour, many of the staff objected strongly to being treated like Boy Scouts with John as the Scout Master. It was intolerable to be required to behave according to the personal code of the D.G. They resented having to be "loyal subjects" at the crack of a whip. While John showed the King the photograph he'd taken of them visiting the Front in 1915, or recited bits of Kipling to the Queen, they moved anxiously from one foot ot the other, waiting for their turn to be introduced. And when it was all over and the Royal couple had gone back to Buckingham Palace, senior staff, men of character and ability, huddled together exchanging wry smiles with politicians who hovered nearby, longing for the moment when John would lose the patronage of the high and mighty.

But from 1932 to 1936, John had the wholehearted support and confidence of first Ramsay MacDonald and secondly, Baldwin. Moreover he had a relationship with Whitley which was that of father and son. And Whitley was highly regarded in political circles. By using his contacts, he was able to remove problems and disagreements with a wave of his wand, like a magician conjuring away warts. In fact the only reservation John had over Whitley, was the pronounced Yorkshire accent of his son. The more he saw of Whitley, the more he liked him, and the more he liked him . . . the more he liked the job of Chairman.

On New Year's Day, 1936, he went into his study and made a list: 1) New Charter in 1936; 2) New Board in 1936 with self as Chairman; 3) New job in 1936 with position in Cabinet. Then he burned it.

When the White Rabbit had finally been ejected from the burrow, John had laughingly said to Nairne, "How about me for your next Chairman?", and Nairne—about his only ally on the Board—had laughingly replied, "Make sure you get more than a Chairman's salary!" It had only been a spontaneous reaction, but it showed that the idea was a possibility worth considering, and when the Red Queen had actually hinted that she'd back John for Chairman—for whatever private reasons—that showed that the seed was germinating. Meanwhile, he'd take advantage of the strong political pressure to reorganise the B.B.C., and start appointing people to key positions, so that when he took over from Whitley, he need only make a few promotions and the chain of command could continue uninterrupted.

He therefore decided to groom Cecil Graves. When Carpendale retired in a year or two, Graves would become Deputy Director General, ready to move into John's office the moment John moved into Whitley's. To maintain continuity, there needed to be a third person who wouldn't be promoted or anything else. He'd be the Manager, like they had on *The Times*. John searched about and did a great deal of praying before finally settling for Colonel Dawnay. The Colonel had been a friend of Lawrence of Arabia who'd given John his Arab shirt as a souvenir on a visit to Broadcasting House, but otherwise there seemed no particular reason for selecting him. It was one of John's rare mistakes. Unlike the Admiral, who managed to combine his notions of naval discipline with a reasonably flexible approach, Dawnay had to work by the book of rules and, as they were all unwritten, he introduced a form of military bureaucracy which was totally at odds with life in the B.B.C. After eighteen months he was replaced, but by then the frustrations and mistrusts among the staff had begun to fester.

John, deliberately distancing himself from direct control, failed to see what was going on. As far as he was concerned he'd got *"Three in One, and One in Three"* like the old hymn—Himself as God the Father, Graves as God the Son, and Dawnay as the Holy Ghost. What could be better than that? But John Reith was not God, and he couldn't possibly foretell the future, even though Miss Nash urged him to consult her astrologer. Nor did he make any real effort to consider the various alternatives. He was like a chess player who has it all worked out, and forgets that he has someone sitting opposite him who can also make a move.

In 1935, Whitley died unexpectedly, and Lord Bridgeman was appointed. When the chairmanship again became vacant due to Bridgeman's speedy retirement through ill health, John's hour seemed to have struck. He'd dropped the broadest of hints to Kingsley Wood, the Postmaster General, on more than one occasion, but his claims to the title were ignored—Ronald Norman, former member of the L.C.C. and brother to Montagu Norman, Governor of the Bank of England, was crowned instead. In public John made him welcome, but privately he damned him. "He's as bad as Clarendon, Musie, if not worse."

"You must try to be friends with him, John," Muriel pleaded, knowing her pleas were useless.

"He's quite gaga, Musie, but I'll do my best." And, after a time, he got on with him quite well, but he missed Whitley personally as a friend whom he knew and trusted. He felt isolated from the Board and relied more and more on Carpendale and Graves and Miss Nash and Jo Stanley. There was no question of a resumption of the Civil War which had torn him apart under Clarendon, but he was unhappy. He'd always been subject to fits of depression, and these now became more frequent, his morbid reflections more dismal.

John wasn't afraid of death for himself. He'd proved that many times during his brief spell at the Front in 1915. It had amused

him to walk out into No Man's Land to have a pee, or walk along
the parapets in order to get a better view of the enemy. He
despised the C.O. who dodged off when the mortars started
thudding over, leaving a full cup of tea! He noted his own hand
hadn't even moved from the word he was writing at the time—
"Destiny". He wasn't even afraid when the bullet struck—only
angry that his best uniform was spattered with blood . . . But he
was afraid that his beloved mother would die, and every so often
noted her age—81, 82, 83, 84, 85, 86, in his diary, as though by
doing so, at least another twelve months would remain to her.

When Jean rang up and told him that Mother had had another
heart attack he flinched away from taking the next train up to
Dumfries, saying that his unexpected arrival might make his
mother worse. Every day he rang up, and the news was always
the same—"No change in her condition". She was 86 and old
age hadn't impaired her faculties at all, except for deafness. She
was very tired. There was a lot of work to be done at the office,
and his mother wasn't going to die. It was December, 1935, and
1936 would be the year of the new Charter. Nothing had been
able to get in the way of the meticulous planning which was the
preamble to securing the renewal of the Charter. He was ready
for the Government enquiry which would take place under the
aged Lord Ullswater, who seemed more concerned with his
garden than anything else . . . John was dictating yet another
memorandum concerning staff pay and conditions, but he felt his
concentration slipping away. He stopped. Miss Nash looked at
him.

"Do you think I ought to go up to Dumfries?" he asked.

"Most certainly I do, Sir John. For your own peace of mind.
And the last time Jean rang me she said Mrs Reith had asked for
you."

"I feel so indecisive. I want to go, and yet I don't." He stood for
a moment looking out at the already darkening street below him.
The Christmas decorations were in the shops. This time of year
filled him with dread. So many of closest and dearest had gone—
and now his mother . . .

"I'll go immediately. Book me a sleeper please, Miss Nash."

He put on his overcoat. It was the one he'd given his father in

1917. He'd had it altered—the tailor used to come to the office for fittings. His father—and now his mother.

Muriel came with him, listening patiently with sympathy. At such a time, she knew he clung on to her, almost like a child.

"I dreamed she was going to live, last night. Her heart is failing, that's all it is. She could have lived for years if it hadn't been for Jean. No that's not true, but that house is so cold and Jean's temperament made Mother unhappy. I wish I had gone up to see her this summer. I didn't show you the letter. It was in the in-tray in the outer office." Muriel looked at a pencilled half sheet, very shakily written. "Love to M and the dear children" she read. There was the usual Churchman's Calendar for 1936 and two little pocket calendars. "Graves has got the obituary notes I made out before we went to America, by the way . . ."

They reached Dumfries at 10.35 a.m. and went straight to the house. Jean opened the door, but they'd been inside for some time before John asked,

"Shall I go up? How is she?"

Jean said, "She passed away at 3.30."

John went up to the bedroom alone. The moment that he'd dreaded most, the sight of his mother's body, was curiously empty. It was just a body he saw, and he almost had to make himself realise that he was looking at the dear face he'd know so long. He remembered the violets he'd brought—still in bud—picked from the rockery by torchlight—he'd thought his mother would be pleased to have them. He laid them on the body and knelt down and prayed.

That night he woke up. Muriel was asleep. He crept out of bed and wrote his diary: "I prayed that I might be worthy of her marvellous love. I kissed the dear forehead and put my ring to her lips. Jean came up and said that Mother had said all sorts of things about what would happen to Jean in the future. I said she need not worry, and kissed her there in Mother's room. I looked out of the window out of which dear Mother had so often looked, and Jean put out some bread in the window box, and lots of tits came down at once. O mater, mater delectissima mea. This your day now and for always. Advent Sunday, December 10th, 1935. How I wish I had gone north before this, that I might have

seen her once again alive, however busy I might be. But I know I
must have no regrets, and I can see her laugh them all away—all
my impatience and unkindness to her. I feel so terribly that I
could almost lose my reason, despite all that people say that I
was so good to her, and all that she has said, I never thought I
was. I always thought I did so very, very little compared to what
I might have done, and what she did for me. This I must also let
her laugh away."

Nobody could laugh away John's feeling of utter loss and
desolation. Muriel reminded him that none of the family or
friends had yet been informed. "Jean should have rung them
up—what can she have been thinking of?" John's feelings of
affection for his sister were short-lived. He got straight on to
Robert who simply said, "So my own sister couldn't be bothered
to let me know", and rang off. John had everything to organise
himself. He missed Douglas—Archie was a broken reed, and
wouldn't be coming up till the day of the funeral. Only Muriel
was any use, making sure that old friends like the Hendersons
and the Bowsers were told immediately. The Hendersons
especially, as she know John wouldn't want to see Maisie and
Charlie.

Soon the B.B.C. was on the line. John had tried to get Cecil
Graves the night before, but he was at church. The duty officer
had proved kind and helpful—John was grateful to him. He felt
closer to them than he did to his own nearest and dearest,
though Robert rang again to apologise for being so short and to
say he was coming by road—ice permitting. And bringing his
son James. Muriel had spoken to the Matron at Chriton and
she'd advised not to tell Ernest till after the funeral. Poor Ernest,
the most brilliant brother of the lot. How his mother must have
doted on him—and now only allowed "downstairs" sometimes
and not able to attend the funeral.

The body had been put in the coffin, and John went upstairs
with the undertaker. He didn't like the brass plate with only
"Ada M. Reith" instead of "Ada Mary" on it. He told Mr Ross to
alter it and arranged with Dr MacGregor to take the service at
the grave. He didn't leave the house till nine, but all the family
came back to the hotel and they had supper together, which John

felt would have pleased his mother.

In the midst of it all, John phoned Mr Ross and told him to add a few words to the brass plate on the coffin. He came back and told the others. "He's going to put 'Mater delectissima' below mother's inscription, which I think is rather nice."

For once all the family were in agreement.

He caught the 11.13 p.m. back to London. He couldn't sleep. He lay there in the darkness, thinking of his mother. He took out the little white handkerchief she'd given him on the station the last time he'd seen her alive. He held it close to his lips, just as he'd held it to her lips before they closed the coffin lid. Her handkerchief would be with him always—folded inside his wallet. His mother was beside him. He lay back, the thumping and thudding of the engine and the rhythmic clunk of the wheels lulling him. But he had a long talk with his mother before he finally fell asleep.

24

Dr Wanner came over. John and Muriel had looked forward to seeing their old friend and hearing news of his family and freely discussing mutual problems inherent in running a broadcasting system. But Dr Wanner's eyes were tired and his hand shook so that he dropped the photographs of Irene and the others sitting by the lake in swimsuits. He was happy to talk about England, and walk in the winter sunshine—though even then he seemed strangely nervous, glancing round. He hardly mentioned Germany.

"You look as if you're frightened of being followed," said John.

"I am, my dear friend. In Germany I am watched all the time. You tell me that you are fearful that the Government will take over control of the B.B.C. next year. In Germany it already has. I am afraid for my wife and my family. Irene is in love with a Nazi. If you write to her, you must be careful."

"Bring her with you on your next visit," said John.

Dr Wanner turned and looked back at Harrias. "I wish to remember your English home and think of it as my English home. I wonder if I shall ever see it again."

The significance of what he said was almost lost on John. The visit had been a disappointment for him, he would be glad when it was over. He gave him a picture of Beaconsfield for Christmas, and gifts for all the girls, and promised that he and Muriel would see them all again very soon. "If Mahommet can come to the mountain, he will," he assured the doctor. They shook hands at the station and parted, never to meet again.

John was himself nervy and anxious. For someone who never suffered from anything worse than toothache, constant indigestion was an intolerable affliction. He had expected it to become worse during and after the funeral, but in fact he didn't have any trouble at all. So he knew it was all "in the mind". He talked it over with Carpendale who advised him to take a holiday. "Go to the South of France instead of me, John. I don't need a holiday, and I'm much happier at home."

John wouldn't hear of it. Miss Nash had resigned so that she could go and see her relatives in India—and the Ullswater Report was due out before Christmas. "I can't leave it to Jo Stanley and you to answer the ludicrous charges that are being levelled against us, Admiral."

"You mean bank charges?" Carpendale made light of it. But he too had heard rumours that the Ullswater Committee would recommend widespread changes throughout the B.B.C.. John walked up and down his office. "I might take a cruise after Christmas. Montagu Norman's asked me to go on his yacht to the Caribbean. Musie thinks it's a good idea. But I'm not sure I want to be shut up for a fortnight with the Governor of the Bank of England."

"Oh, Ronald told me there'll be plenty of young people on board, and Montagu's a very good host. You'll enjoy it."

"I must go down to Folkestone to see Miss Nash off to India." John left the office abruptly. "Come on Miss Stanley."

Carpendale remained in the office—forgotten by John, who seemed totally preoccupied with ensuring that the presents he'd bought for Miss Nash were properly wrapped and that they got to Folkestone in time to give her a surprise send-off.

The Admiral was not much concerned at John's inordinate interest in Miss Nash's departure. If the average Director General took his whole family away for the day in order to wave goodbye to his secretary, the average deputy director might easily regard his conduct as abnormal—particularly when matters of life and death were left behind at the office. But Carpendale knew his boss was only trying to compensate for the speedy manner in which he'd accepted Miss Nash's resignation, telling her she might as well go right away. Miss Nash had been very hurt.

No, what worried Carpendale was how to keep John on an even keel, so that he could deal with the enormous political

pressures which were already being brought to bear upon the
B.B.C.. In ten years there had been three elections, and the B.B.C.
had become the most powerful voice in the land. Churchill was
only one of many who felt hard done by. John had refused to let
him broadcast his views on India, ignoring his hopeful remark, "I
believe you are a friend, Sir John". Prime Ministers, Archbishops,
Chancellors and foreign office spokesmen, had all been denied
access to the precious microphone. Newspaper barons had lost
valuable advertising revenue to the *Radio Times,* and business
interests looked enviously abroad to the vast commercial networks which were making fortunes for their owners. Only John
Reith stood in the way of a bonanza all round, and he badly
needed time to rest and recover his equilibrium. Yet he refused
to rest, refused to take advantage of the offer of a magnificent
holiday on Montagu Norman's millionaire yacht.

When John got back from Folkestone he went straight to
Carpendale's office and said: "I've been thinking of what you
said, Charles. I think you're right. I need a holiday. I'll go after
Christmas. I've changed my mind, so don't say I'm inflexible!"

Perhaps it was the sight of Miss Nash, waving as instructed
from a position behind the funnel, which had made John crave
for a sea voyage. At any rate, he rang Montagu Norman, whom
he hardly knew, and accepted his kind invitation to join his
cruise to Barbados.

Christmas intervened. Christmas the dreaded time, made more
dreadful by the death of his mother. John worked hard to make
it a happy time, sending 200 cards and getting 201 back. He went
shopping and bought everyone a present. He decorated the
Christmas tree with the children, but it was all a hollow and
bogus joy. Left alone for one minute and he thought his heart
would burst in misery. Muriel knew of his feelings and understood, but also knew that she couldn't cope with them alone. So
she filled the house with relatives, and invited children to a
Christmas Party for Christopher and Marista.

John's feeling of gloom and dejection only increased. After
he'd forced a few mouthfuls of Christmas Cake down, he left the
table and went to his study. The Ullswater Report lay unopened
on his desk. He spent all that remained of Christmas Day reading

it in detail, absorbing and analysing the entire contents. On Boxing Day he roughed out a memorandum, and the following day Miss Stanley took twelve hours of dictation. Three days later when members of the Board of Governors returned from the Christmas break, they found copies of the Director General's memorandum on their desks.

John didn't celebrate New Year's Eve, 1935. There were too many painful memories. Instead he wrote in his diary that he hoped he would be a better father and kinder to Muriel. He seemed to have given up so much to the Ullswater Report. He missed his mother desperately—his life seemed meaningless without her. But he would go on—Christopher and Marista needed him for the minimum of another twenty years.

In January, George V died. John's voice was etched into the minds of millions of his fellow subjects as he announced repeatedly, "The King's life is drawing to its close." He was sad and dejected that his name was not mentioned in the New Year's Honours list. Ramsay MacDonald had gone and Baldwin was back. But he was surrounded by the anti-B.B.C. faction—by Kingsley Wood and Chamberlain.

It was February before the Board of Governors were free from their other duties to consider the Ullswater Report in detail— what proposals they would accept and what reject. John made certain they understood exactly that under no circumstances would he tolerate any Government interference whatever. He then gathered up his papers and told them that he was setting sail forthwith for Treasure Island and left them still debating.

The Governors heaved a sigh of relief. It was not relief that as regards the Ullswater Report, John had done all the basic work, and they only had to follow where he led. It was a universal and prolonged sigh of relief that he would be away for three weeks.

John spend a large amount of the cruise in the company of Helen Moir, the young and attractive daughter of a neighbour in Beaconsfield. Together they leant on the ship's rails one evening and watched Jamaica slip past.

"What are you thinking?" asked Helen.

"I'm thinking of my misspent youth," John replied. "By which

Silly Critics of the B.B.C.

In dramatic contrast to the silly outcry which Sir John Reith had to face in the Commons on Monday night, raised by Dishard M.P.s who profess to detect evidence of "Red" sympathies in the B.B.C. announcements.

The overwhelming majority of ordinary listeners would agree without hesitation that the B.B.C. announcements are almost the last place in the world where they would expect to find revolutionary sentiment.

But to the suspicious all things are suspect ; and Sir John Reith has to waste good time and tact to soothe apprehensions which have no existence whatever except in the critics' fantastic imaginations.

The Boys He Knew

"It is read in the course of a train or car journey. And quite a number of emotions again. Nation. Masses of names.

"Here and there, maybe after closest scrutiny and some cogitation, a familiar or once familiar name. Is that the fellow one knew long since? What has he done? Married—received an honour of some sort—got a new job—passed from the sight of men? Oh, well.

"I have just read, for instance, that Captain W. S. Chalmers has been appointed Director at the Royal Naval Staff College at Greenwich. Very nice, too. I used to know him and I admired him a lot.

"To my surprise and gratification, I was invited to join a select body termed the 'Juvenile Sporting Club' of which he was the centre and inspiration.

"When Chalmers left for Dartmouth the club, so to speak, left with him, I did not see him again for 14 years.

It Was During the War

"One late afternoon in March, 1916, I was riding with two N.C.O.s along a road near Bois Grenier, three-quarters of a mile or so behind our front-line trench.

"A shell passed over us. An odd one. Just one for the moment.

"Having nothing better to do we proceeded to investigate. What was our surprise to discover a sort of armoured train with two enormous guns mounted thereon.

"We dismounted, and with one of my companions I crossed a field for a nearer view. An officer emerged. His rig was strange; it was mostly khaki, but as he approached we failed at first to identify the insignt or rank or regiment.

"Royal Navy. This was terrific news. I think we expected to be warned off, but found ourselves civilly addressed.

"The Story appeared amiable and in conversational mood. Eventually we were but expect his madness.

"On taking grateful leave, we were asked, 'Is the 9th Scottish Rifles anywhere near here?'

"'It was,' we replied, and moreover we belonged to it. 'But you're touching once.' I explained that I was transport officer, and my companion one of the transport corporals.

"'Is Stanley Smith out with you?' Yes, he was. Will you tell him I am asking for him? My name's Chalmers.

"'Willie Chalmers?' I said. 'That's the sort of thing the Chronicle does.'

And Sir John Said—

Sir John Reith Answers Charges of "Bias"
B.B.C.'S CRITICS
IMPARTIALITY HIS AIM

FACTS

Sir John Reith, £7,500 a year Director-General of the B.B.C. is generally recognised as real controller of British broadcasting. A son of the manse, he was trained as an engineer, but forsook this profession to found B.B.C. in 1922. Rumoured that he will receive peerage in Coronation Honours. Age 46.

Sir John Reith Answers His Critics in the House

B.B.C. ADVISORY COMMITTEE OF M.P.s PROPOSED

By the Political Correspondent DAVID KEIR

FOR the best part of an hour and a quarter last night Sir John Reith, Director-General of the B.B.C., faced his critics in the House of Commons at a private meeting of Conservative M.P.s.

Most of the critics were the well-known "Colonel Blimps" of Parliament—men who seem to spend their week-ends listening for traces of "Red bias" in the polished utterances of B.B.C. announcers.

To these Sir John Reith put up the defence that, while there were occasional "slip-ups" in phraseology, on the whole both news and talks were designed to satisfy listeners of all parties.

It was gathered after the meeting that numbers generally were very satisfied with Sir John Reith's explanation, and that he handled the situation with great success, although a minority of the meeting was not perhaps fully convinced that the B.B.C. could not have been more impartial.

B.B.C. AND IMPARTIALITY.

Sir John Reith was able to persuade a meeting of the 1922 Committee of Conservatives at the House of Commons, last night, of the general impartiality of the B.B.C. programmes. We should say there will be public assent to his statement that the main object of the B.B.C. after which it is always striving, is to be impartial. The programmes convey that impression, but perhaps no amount of care could quite eliminate from every mind all belief to the contrary. One criticism was directed to a talk in the educational part of a programme by a learned professor, and it was the subject of questions in Parliament. The talk may in fact have seemed to some to lean too heavily to one particular side. But it seems clear that if talks are to have the quality of liveness some latitude of thought to individuals must be admitted. The essential question is whether on the whole a fair balance of view is secured over the whole range of talks. Admittedly that, with the best intention in the world, cannot be an easy task. The public will trust to the B.B.C. and Sir John Reith to do their best in the matter. With an audience almost co-terminous with the nation the B.B.C. no doubt see the point of full impartiality as clearly as anyone else. But they are certainly under the obligation not only to have good intentions but to convey the impression of having them and of doing their best to act upon them. If any sort of check is necessary it may be found in the Parliamentary advisory committee which Sir John Reith suggested. That would certainly be a better solution than the increase of direct Parliamentary control which some have suggested. Quiet friendly advice is more suited to this particular little problem—if problem it can be called—than regulation by the concentrated majesty of Parliament.

B.B.C. CHIEF REPLIES TO HIS CRITICS

COL. BLIMP AND THE B.B.C.

To meet certain criticisms of the alleged "redness" of News Bulletins, the B.B.C. is about to appoint a new announcer whose well-known fairness of tone and view should satisfy the most rampantly "impartial" anti-red.

"Gad, listeners, Reuter, the Central News and Exchange are right! the Madrid Government and the dirty skunks, and their altruistic army is in flight. Three impartial cheers for Franco !"

JOHN REITH,
Director-General of the B.B.C., addressed 1922 Committee of Conservative M.P.s at the House of Commons last night, and replied to allegations of bias in recent news and educational broadcasts.

---

9. Cuttings from Reith's scrapbook

20. *Reith and Montagu Norman and family*

21. *The Bowser family photograph used in a Christmas greeting card, 1937*

22.   *Christopher Reith*

23.   *Reith and Marista boating*

B.B.C. Chief Delights His Chief As "Bookie" Staff

BEST WISHES FOR YOUR SUCCESS TONIGHT STOP WOULD LIKE SCREEN TEST FOR YOU IF SUITABLE YOU REPLACE ERIC BLORE AS BUTLER WITH ASTAIRE AND ROGERS IN NEXT PICTURE

M H AYLESWORTH

MY BEST WISHES FOR A MOST SUCCESSFUL DEBUT LENOX P LOHR

PRESIDENT NATBROCAST

Sir John Reith Smiles, And The Staff Smiles With Him

SIR JOHN REITH strode into the entrance hall of Broadcasting House yesterday morning.

He beamed smiles on the commissionaires as they sprang to attention and saluted. They even dared to smile back at him.

And afterwards, as he disappeared from their view, ven-

SIR JOHN REITH in two

SIR JOHN REITH BRINGS DOWN HOUSE

B.B.C. STAFF IN "I HAVE no desire, sir, to DRAMA dictate to the staff, nor to interfere in their private lives."

24. These cuttings from Reith's scrapbook show a lighter side

I don't mean what you think I mean."

Helen giggled and sipped her martini. John sipped at his whisky, to which he'd been introduced by Montagu Norman, along with sherry and cocktails. "I mean that I've never been young. It was not the fault of my strict upbringing. I was always wanting to take on the responsibilities and authority of someone twice my age."

"Do you regret your misspent youth, Sir John?"

"Very much. But I'm enjoying myself now." He looked round to see Helen's boyfriend approaching. "Here comes Corduroy to interrrupt our tête á tête." He made room for his rival who talked about flying fish while John, smitten as ever by guilt, wondered what Muriel would think if she knew he'd taken to the bottle after a lifetime on the waggon. He decided he'd write her a long letter and tell her that Montagu Norman had recommended whisky for medicinal purposes and that it had indeed settled his stomach. In fact he felt better than he had for months. He liked Montagu and his wife, and the other guests were to his taste as well, quite a feat, as he was the first to admit. He was grateful for all the kindness and attention. Nobody even faintly suggested that he was on the cruise for the benefit of his health, but he watched over his own symptoms of what he called "accidie", and noted that the depression said to have afflicted many a mediaeval monk, had lifted.

The same concern to ensure John's return to health was also very much uppermost in the minds of those he'd left in charge at the B.B.C.. So determined were John's immediate entourage that their chief should be released from all pressure, that they had, even before he went on the cruise, agreed not to burden him with day-to-day administrative problems. Unfortunately one of the problems they decided to deal with on their own was not merely one of administration. It involved principles and personalities—one in particular—Richard S. Lambert, editor of *The Listener*.

If John was the founder of the B.B.C., Lambert occupied a similar position as regards *The Listener*, and like John he resented all forms of interference with his magazine. ·They got on quite well, John deliberately confining his interference to corrections in punctuation and grammar, and writing the odd article himself. When John and Muriel went to dinner at his house, they found Lambert very much a family man with a wide range of interests outside the B.B.C. which included being on the Board of the Film Institute. John who always maintained that he preferred his employees to have another job, so that he could sack them without compunction, had no objection to Lambert working for the Film Institute provided he didn't use his position at the B.B.C. to promote his films. Lambert was also interested in the occult, and John, believing like Hamlet that "there are more things in Heaven and Earth than are dreamed of in your vocabulary" read with amusement the series of articles written by Harry Price, the well-known ghost-hunter. The general public were amused too, and the circulation of *The Listener* increased.

The last of these special reports concerned a mongoose on the Isle of Man which was credited with being able to talk in several languages. Lambert and Harry Price had been over to see for themselves and published a full account of their adventures in a small book called *The Haunting of Cashends Gap*. Nothing more might have been heard of "the talking mongoose" had not Lambert related the story in person to the Chairman of the Film Institute, Sir Cecil Levita. Though very deaf, he heard enough to decide that Lambert was mad "Damn it, he believes it!"—and set about getting Lambert off the Film Board, by enlisting the aid of the B.B.C. to bring pressure to bear on an employee.

Levita asked Gladstone Murray to lunch with him at the Carlton. Murray was no longer Public Relations Officer, but Levita had known him as such when on the L.C.C., and assumed that a word in his ear would be enough. What he didn't realise was that Gladstone Murray, after being heir presumptive to the throne, had fallen from grace. Starting with his handling of the Peter Eckersley business, John had begun to distrust him, and had finally removed him from power (though not from the B.B.C.) after Murray had held a large party solely in order to bring together all the disaffected members and ex-members of the Staff.

Murray listened with apparent sympathy to Sir Cecil's off-the-record diatribe against his friend, and immediately afterwards

summoned Lambert to his office and told him that Sir Cecil
Levita didn't think he was a suitable person to be a Governor of
the National Film Institute, and therefore, by imputation,
shouldn't be the Editor of *The Listener*.

Lambert was horrified. He was entirely dependent on his job
with the B.B.C., and in February, 1936, an out-of-work editor was
likely to remain so. "What do you think I should do?" he asked
the much more worldly Murray.

"Tell Sir Cecil that he either retracts immediately and apolo-
gises, or you'll put the matter in the hands of your solicitors."

Sir Cecil didn't retract, and by the time John returned from his
cruise, Lambert had issued a writ for slander.

Sir Stephen Tallents broke the news to the Director General
on March 1st. The new King had been on a visit to Broadcasting
House, and John was in an affable mood. Sir Stephen had reason
to select his moment, for it was he, in his capacity as Public
Relations Controller, who had told Lambert to go ahead with his
action. Later on, when he realised that the B.B.C. might be drawn
in, he'd had second thoughts.

John listened in silence. There was something about Sir
Stephen Tallents he didn't much like. Perhaps his total unruffa-
bility, his enigmatic smile, his diplomatic smoothness. He'd been
connected with the Postmaster General's office—was he also
connected with the hated Kingsley Wood? John's immediate
reaction was not to criticise Lambert's behaviour. It was Tallents
who had handled the affair most ineptly.

"If he asks to see me, I'll see him. If not—not."

"He wants to see the Chairman," said Tallents.

"In that case, let him see the Chairman." John felt a spasm of
irritation which was probably the prelude to the indigestion
which had left him during the cruise.

After supper he complained to Muriel. "I've got it again. I'm
paying the price for the maddening incompetence of a lot of
ex'civil service bureaucrats. Nothing to do with the B.B.C."

But in the weeks that followed the B.B.C. became more and
more enmeshed. Harold Brown was a governor, and an old
friend of Sir Cecil. His help was sought to bring Lambert to heel,
and he agreed to bring the matter before the Board. Sir Cecil's

solicitors then wrote off to Lambert asking him not to do anything more until the outcome of the meeting, thereby providing him with just the proof he needed to show that the B.B.C. was interfering with the liberty of the subject to act according to his conscience. Sir Cecil rushed off to see Ronald Norman at his home, and Sir Stephen Tallents made matters worse by interviewing Lambert and telling him, "Frankly, if you go on with the case, there's a serious danger that you may prejudice your position with the B.B.C.."

By now Lambert had developed a certain cunning under the tutelage of Gladstone Murray. He asked Tallents to put it in writing. Tallents did, and the stage was set for a confrontation which would go far beyond Sir Cecil's original ill-advised remarks to Gladstone Murray. Nevertheless, Lambert asked to see the Director General.

John realised the seriousness of the situation. He regarded the whole thing as utterly ridiculous, and told Carpendale that Lambert was obviously quite mad, but he knew that unless the case was settled out of court, the B.B.C. must inevitably be dragged in. "If it was left to me," said the Admiral, "I'd let him get whatever's bothering him off his chest and send him off on leave."

"You think he's sick?"

"Fraying at the edges. I'd label him 'fragile—handle with care'."

"Well, I don't want to weaken the B.B.C.'s case if we've got to have one, and I don't want things to go by default any more, Charles. I shall keep the conversation unofficial, and there'll be no persuasion. Lambert has a strong, if subterranean, vanity and egotism." He smiled. "I remember meeting him on the stairs. He stood two steps up, so as to be on a level with me. I'll make sure we meet as equals."

Meeting as equals meant that John roamed about his office, while Lambert sat bolt upright in the Queen Anne chair opposite the huge desk. "Do you want this discussion to be official or personal, Lambert?"

"Personal."

"The first I heard about all this was seven weeks after you

went to see Tallents. And frankly I'm amazed that having told you to go ahead with a writ for slander he then told you not to. I regret that I didn't handle it from the start."

"So do I. I've always regarded you as the natural protector of the Staff—a friend at Court."

John sat down at his desk and surveyed Lambert. It seemed to him that the editor was speaking lines that he'd rehearsed. "Friend at Court" was very much the sort of spurious flattery that Gladstone Murray would have used. "I'm afraid that heads of departments are more and more dealing directly with members of the Staff and with Governors."

"The truth is that Sir Stephen Tallents is no good," Lambert said, unexpectedly. "Others agree with me."

"What others? Eckersley, Gladstone Murray, Nichols?" he had been suspicious about the head of Administration for some time. "Farquhar, Chapman and Peacock?" He picked up the phone. "Which of them would you like to speak to?"

"I don't wish to involve anybody else in my predicament."

John put the phone down and leant forward. "Get this into your mind, Lambert. Neither I nor the Chairman, nor the Vice Chairman have the least interest in Sir Cecil Levita. The advice you have been given to drop the case was in your own interests and in the interests of the Corporation."

"All right, I accept your word for that. I'm quite prepared to adopt any other solution if you'll meet my conditions."

"What are they?"

Lambert took out a piece of paper, and read from it. "1) I can carry through my work at the Film Institute. 2) I want satisfaction from Sir Cecil Levita. 3) My position as Editor of *The Listener* and as an employee of the B.B.C. to be in no way prejudiced."

"Very fair. As far as I'm concerned you can start *de nova* from the moment."

"But you may leave," said Lambert.

John reassured him. "If I am committed, the Corporation is committed."

"I still feel there's not much future for me after all this."

The man was obviously confused. "In that case you should leave, but not till all this trouble is over. You must sail out on an even keel. I won't advise you further unless I'm sure you want me to. And even then I'm not sure I will," he added.

"Why not?"

"You may not think my advice disinterested."

"I think very highly of you."

John got up again and offered Lambert a cigarette. He lit it for him and went over to the window. "Mr Lambert, something will have to be done to clear the good name of the B.B.C. There's a lot of talk going around, and I understand the matter may be raised in the House."

"Yes."

"Who by?"

"Friends."

John turned and looked at him. "Friends," he repeated in a melancholy voice. The friends who would shortly be regaled by Lambert's account of this meeting. The friends who were determined to bring Sir John Reith and his B.B.C. to their knees. "I'll write you a letter," he said.

Lambert seemed momentarily taken by surprise. "I'd like your advice now, sir."

"I prefer to think it over. I'll see you tomorrow."

"That's a Saturday. You'll have to come especially."

"I'll be delighted to."

Lambert hesitated. Perhaps he was thinking of his family. Did he want to consult with his 'friends'? "Or would you prefer Monday?" John asked politely.

"Monday would be better."

"Then let's say the Athenaeum at 7.30 for dinner."

They shook hands.

On Monday morning there was a note from Lambert in Miss Stanley's "In" tray. He apologised for changing his mind. As the first three minutes had not yielded a salary increment, there seemed no point in continuing the discussion. "Salary increment!" John was irritated. He should have remembered that. The Board had decided to withhold it, pending the outcome . . . There was no putting the clock back. There was a P.S.: "I am so certain of the justice of my case that I am ready to put my character and conduct in issue by raising the matter in court."

"Oh well," thought John, "at least Muriel and I can have dinner together for once."

Muriel was always warned by John if he was coming home early or staying late at the office. He was most considerate in that respect. On the other hand, he only came home early when there'd been some trouble at the B.B.C.. Muriel was expected to be there waiting for him, ready, quite literally—to hold his hand as they walked round the garden together.

Muriel and John sat on a garden seat.

"Just smell those roses," John sniffed the air appreciatively. He didn't know a marigold from a tulip, but he tried to show interest for Muriel's sake. Gardening for John consisted of pruning the laurels, sawing logs and stacking them according to size and length, and telling Clark what to do about the lawn mower.

"What will you do with Mr Lambert now?" Muriel asked.

"Send him on his grace leave. He's due for it after ten years. He looks to me as though he's far from well. I don't want to be accused of his premature demise as well as everything else." He sighed. "What he needs is a double dose of syrup of figs."

"That's the answer to everything," said Muriel, even with a hint of a smile, and kissed him. He felt better. "We'll soon be on holiday," she whispered.

"Holiday—what do you mean, holiday? I've just had one. What do you think that cruise was?" His feelings of contentment and cheerfulness vanished at the prospect of a family holiday by the sea.

"I've booked us for three weeks in Hunstanton."

"Hunstanton! But we went there the year before last and I said 'Never again.' "

"John dear, it's only three weeks and the children will love it."

"I won't. Freezing cold. Nothing to do all day but walk up and down the beach picking up litter."

"You don't have to," Muriel pleaded.

"I prefer it to sitting wrapped up in a deckchair waiting for the dinner gong to sound."

Muriel burst out, "John, why do you have such a jaundiced view of life?"

"There's no life at Hunstanton, jaundiced or otherwise, except for that day I met the Archbishop of Canterbury shrimping."

Muriel laughed and John got up. "I'll go and feed the hens," he said.

She watched his tall majestic frame striding towards the paddock. She heard him summoning the hens towards the Harrods' henhouse. After that, the Director General of the B.B.C. would collect up the eggs, wash them and meticulously enter the numbers of a graph in his study. And, at the end of the day, he'd write his diary, and among wars and earthquakes, Prime Ministers and Presidents, he would record the name of some non-laying hen who had failed in her duty.

25

As long as the 'Case of the Talking Mongoose' was *sub judice*, John could be fairly sure that the B.B.C. would not be singled out for attack. Besides, Parliament was in recess. But he was under no illusions as to the sort of thing he might expect once Lambert's libel action had been heard—even if he lost, which was always a possibility. As long ago as April 29th, he'd sat in the Strangers' Gallery to listen to the Commons first debate on the Ullswater Report, and heard Sir Stafford Cripps fulminating against the B.B.C.: "What right have they got to use their economic power on Mr Lambert? This behaviour is not merely a matter for condemnation, it's a grave scandal, and something which the House ought to take notice of!" He'd been surprised by this outburst, but even more surprised at the warm reception accorded to Sir Stafford, not merely by Labour M.P.s like Attlee, but by numerous Conservatives. From the way they looked up at him, he knew that his presence was noted. He longed for a champion to rise to his feet as Lloyd George had done ten years before and decimate the opposition with a fusillade of scorn. But it was John Reith who rose to his feet and left the Chamber, without a word.

Ever since there had been newspaper articles and cartoons which kept the public generally informed about the progress of events. The pot was kept simmering, and by the time Sir Cecil Levita entered the witness box, all England was crowding round him, like fielders round the last man in.

John did not share their hilarity as they read the reports. He knew that Lambert had not only friends working for him in the B.B.C., but men of great influence outside. Men prepared to give money towards the cause. Lambert did not jib at the extreme right-wing views of one of his benefactors from the House of Lords, nor to making use of his own secretary to copy out dictated memos on every word spoken to him by John. He who complained of interference with his private conscience had dossiers on everyone with whom he came in contact for incorporation in his counsel's brief.

John was subpoena'd as a witness, and wrote out a memo for himself. In his opinion, Lambert "has a strong vein of the fanatic in him. He believes that the cause justifies the means, and that he is striking a blow for the freedom of the individual against a Corporation that has betrayed him. He feels that he now has a duty to strike a blow for the freedom of the Press, and wants to play for public sympathy". When John's turn came to speak, he was determined to let the judge know what kind of man it was who was putting the whole future of the B.B.C. in jeopardy in order to satisfy his personal egotism and vanity.

Lambert's counsel were perhaps wise not to call the Director General. Sir Patrick Hastings knew exactly what line to take against Sir Cecil Levita, fumbling with his hearing aids. He made everybody in England laugh at him. Sir Cecil was exposed as a credulous old fool who accused the editor of *The Listener* of being mad enough to believe in a mongoose that could talk, not only in English, but Russian, Hebrew, Hindustani, Welsh and Manx! A clairvoyant mongoose who knew about cars and aeroplanes, could dance and play ball, only killed rabbits out of season, and claimed that it was the Holy Ghost.

By the time the case was over and Lambert had received £7,500 in compensation, it was not only Sir Cecil Levita who was being held up to ridicule, it was Sir John Reith. Had not the B.B.C. taken the side of Levita, threatening Lambert with loss of job if he didn't withdraw? Hadn't they written to him even, warning him to give up or face the consequences? And who was the ultimate authority, who dictated the way the B.B.C. was run? John Reith. Sir Cecil Levita left the box minus £7,500, but the Director General of the B.B.C. took his place in the public mind. Nothing would satisfy Lambert's supporters but a Cabinet Inquiry to consider, not only the Ullswater Recommendations, but the whole basis upon which the Charter of the B.B.C. rested and might be renewed.

Muriel was having breakfast when John came in from his study. He'd been reading the newspapers with customary distaste. Only *The Times* ranked worthy of respect. It was usually carefully folded to be read on the train, while the others were carried by their ears at arm's length. "Like dead rats" was little Marista's precocious way of putting it. Today, even *The Times* seemed to have a bad smell and was laid to rest on the sideboard while John poured himself coffee.

Muriel decided to take no notice, and helped Christopher open a packet of holiday snaps which had just come with the post. "Oh, these are some of the ones you took on the cruise, John."

"Mr Boot's taken long enough." He settled in his chair at the head of the table and opened *The Times* with a sigh. "Don't put your dirty finger marks all over them, C.J.."

"They're not dirty." Christopher refused to be put down so early in the morning.

"Don't argue boy!" He read in ponderous tones: "The atmosphere inside the B.B.C. is unhealthy, overwrought and morbid. In the entrance hall a carved stone proclaims that the B.B.C. is dedicated to 'Almighty God—John Reith being the first Director General'. God's Director General, one assumes."

"Go on," said Muriel warily.

John handed the paper over to her. "No. Read it for yourself, how the rest of the world sees your husband." He stubbed his finger at the leader column. Muriel put her glasses on to read: "Favouritism and intrigue are the means by which the internal administration is carried on.' It's only some beastly politician John."

"Lambert is not a politician. That's where it comes from. I thought the Mongoose Case was closed, but evidently Mr Lambert thinks otherwise. He and his friends are making a last-ditch attempt to stop us getting our new Charter. Listen to this! It was the turn of the *Daily Express* "At Question Time, M.P.s from all parties were agreed. The new Charter must not be a licence for Sir John Reith to enjoy another ten years of what he's been pleased to call 'Monopoly under God'. Above all, he must not be allowed to rule his subjects like a dictator."

"Whoever said that?" Muriel was genuinely upset.

"Our louse-ridden Postmaster General, of course. 'The B.B.C. under the guidance of Sir John Reith, is the nearest thing in this country to government by the Nazis!'" He flung the paper down, making the cups shake. "And I'm supposed to give evidence before the Cabinet Committee after they've read all that!"

Marista glanced at Christopher. She wanted to see the photographs and was waiting her opportunity to speak as soon as the storm passed. "Show them to Marista, Christopher," said Muriel. They quickly forgot the outburst. They were accustomed to taking shelter and then creeping back as though nothing had happened.

Muriel looked at the ones taken on board Sir Montagu Norman's yacht. "They all seem to be of Helen Moir."

"Well, she was the only thing worth looking at."

"You seem to have been looking at her rather a lot." Muriel's normally mild tones had a slightly acid tinge to them.

John looked at the photograph appreciatively. "She's young and beautiful—don't be jealous."

Christopher passed mother another snap. She reacted almost with outrage. "This one's at Ascot, John!"

He looked over her shoulder. "So it is—do you like her hat?"

"You took her to Ascot!"

"Yes, and you know perfectly well I took Jo Stanley to the *Housemaster* and Sybil What's It to the Eldorado—you remember that little restaurant at Windsor—we used to go there a lot."

"What's it like?" Muriel didn't even try to keep her sense of injury to herself.

"Not a patch on what it was. Very seedy."

"I'm sorry to hear that. It used to be our very special place."

John gathered up his unopened letters in irritation. "You could have come if you'd wanted to, Musie. But you never want to go anywhere. Be honest—you're not gregarious—I am—that's the difference."

"I'm not discontented, that's the difference."

The children huddled together. Another squall. John was angry. "I'm, not having an affair. I'm not being unfaithful. . !"

"John please! The children are here."

"Bother the children!" He walked to the door and turned. "You're jealous because I enjoy the company of young women because they cheer me up and make me laugh—which you never do!"

He went out through the hall, collecting his hat and umbrella. The door slammed.

Muriel got up from the table. "Come on, let's wave goodbye to Daddy."

"Why should you?" Christopher looked rebellious.

"Because I always do," said Muriel simply. "He'd think there was something wrong if I didn't."

The three of them went to the front door step. He was halfway down the drive, shouting loudly to the trees, "I want to climb the Cairngorms! I hate Beaconsfield! It's so flat and boring." He stopped and looked back. "Boring, boring, boring!"

Muriel waved back at him and John raised his hat on his umbrella in salute.

On the train, John found a compartment and started to read Lees-Smith's speech during the debate. The former Postmaster General told Whitley before the latter became B.B.C. Chairman that he would have to work in harness with a Director General who was rapidly going off his head. It seemed to John that Lees Smith was himself going mad. "In return for the Charter, this House must demand a Staff Association!" He looked over his newspaper at the dark-suited city gents sitting opposite to him. It seemed to him that they were only waiting to engage him in conversation. They usually did when there was something more than average about the B.B.C. or himself in their morning paper.

He read on. "If I talk with an employee of the B.B.C., I am made to feel like a conspirator—friends I have known for years look round to see if they're being followed. I must not use the telephone—it will be tapped—I may not write letters, they will be opened."

The wretched divorce lawyer tapped him on his knee.

"Parliamentary privilege seems to allow them to get away with the most abominable accusations, Sir John."

John got up. "Excuse me." He found the man physically repellent and sought refuge in the guard's van. His friend there only read the football pages. He was a Scotsman and reminded John of Shorty, his fellow apprentice on the shop floor at the locomotive works. John had no ability whatever when it came to handling nuts and bolts or anything else that might have been regarded as the least mechanical. Shorty had saved him from disgrace on more than one occasion. The train guard saved him now.

As he stood, leaning against the window, bumping and rattling to Marylebone, he made a plan of campaign. He knew that now that Gladstone Murray had gone off to Canada to manage broadcasting there, and Nichols the crook had removed himself after collecting £6,000 as compensation, there only remained one key witness—Richard Lambert. Obviously he wouldn't withdraw the allegations which were at the heart of his libel action, but he might be persuaded to bury the hatchet.

He walked through the main entrance of the B.B.C. at exactly nine o'clock. Kilroy was there to greet him, the lift doors kept open for his arrival, page-boys standing at a respectful distance. Usually John would have a word with anyone who happened to be waiting for the other lift. He prided himself on knowing the names of most of the people who worked in the building, and as he listened to the programmes whenever he could, he often took the opportunity to congratulate some lowly reporter or actor on his performance. He tried hard to keep a sense of being one of the family, rather than head of a great corporation, but it was not like the good old days at Savoy Hill, where he'd travel on the Underground and, if he encountered a member of staff, they'd walk to work together, and John would ask him what he did and how he liked it, and where he lived and so on. Today the famous scowl covered his face and nobody said more than "Good Morning, Sir John". Secretly he was amused. He knew what they were thinking. As the lift doors closed he raised his arm in the Nazi salute and said, "Heil Hitler!" The main entrance hall of the B.B.C. exploded with laughter.

Carpendale was already waiting in the office. He greeted John impassively. "Morning, John."

"Read the papers, Charles? The Admiral nodded gravely. "Don't worry—they're only taking a sideways swipe at us to knock Baldwin off his perch. Neville Chamberlain, Lees-Smith and Attlee, united in their hatred of me. Rats gnawing at the foundations." Miss Stanley came in with the mail. "Miss Stanley, tell Mr Lambert I want to see him immediately."

Carpendale put a sealed envelope on the desk. "My resignation, sir."

"Resignation?" John didn't even open it. "Don't be daft man. If there's any resigning to be done, I'll do it. Do you think I'd make a good Viceroy of India? Trouble is Muriel's so shy. I don't see her sitting on an ivory throne. Which reminds me." He picked up the phone. "Put a call through to Mr de Lotbiniere, Mrs Bottle. Outside Broadcast."

"I'm serious, John, I'm far too old. You need new blood."

"New blood? You make me sound like a vampire. That's one epithet the papers haven't thought of. No, no, Charles, it's out of the question. This is the crucial moment—I need you more than ever."

The Admiral was not to be put off. "John, the Government wants a change in our régime, so they can all go home and say they've won—all the weeks of jaw-jaw and palaver and enquiries have not been wasted. They'll have a new Board of Governors, a Staff Association . . ."

"Never! A Staff Association simply builds up secret divisions and jealousies. If a member of the staff complains to me about another, I say: 'Don't tell me—tell him' I pick up the phone and bring them eyeball to eyeball. That's the honest, decent way to go about things."

Carpendale persisted. "But if I, as Deputy Director resign, the Government will be able to appoint one of their own men to be your successor one day."

"My successor, eh?" John took Carpendale by the hand. "I'm not going, and neither are you."

The phone went. "Oh good morning, Lobby. Apropos of what we were discussing the other day." The King's romance with Mrs

Simpson was well known to nearly everybody who had anything to do with the Royal Household, and de Lotbiniere and John had already had long conversations about how to deal with the situation should a constitutional crisis emerge. "If the King asks you to set up a broadcast from anywhere else—refer him to me."

"I've already worked out a plan," said de Lotbiniere.

John smiled. It was typical of the Head of Outside Broadcasting to make his own arrangements without consulting anyone. That was what John expected from his lieutenants. He contented himself with a mild rebuke: "Who's in charge of this outfit, Lobby—you or me? The King cannot broadcast without the Prime Minister's permission and mine. If he comes round here himself, I shall personally refuse permission for him to broad-cast. Is that understood?"

He put the phone down without waiting for a reply. In a way he felt sorry for the King, besotted with that wretched Simpson woman. He said to Carpendale, "You know, Charles, when I saw the Prince of Wales in the trenches, I thought of him as my future King and Emperor. I would cheerfully have laid down my life for him!" He was suddenly angry, "He has no right to cast away the crown of England and trample it in the mire!"

Carpendale was surprised at the outburst. He accepted John's deeply felt principles as regards the monarchy, but the anger he displayed at that moment went far beyond patriotic fervour. It worried him that his friend seemed to have so much intensity of feelings bottled up inside.

The change was almost immediate. "I shan't accept your resignation, Charles. Once the Charter is ours and the battle won, you can retire in good order as befits a naval officer." He tore up the still unread letter. "I am confident that when I go before the Cabinet Committee this afternoon, I shall carry the day—same as I've always done—one man against the lot of them."

Jo Stanley entered. "Mr Lambert's here, Sir John."

"Oh good. Ask him to wait will you?"

Miss Stanley hesitated. "He . . . he says he's very busy sir.'

"Good. Ask him to wait." He noticed the Admiral's quizzical look. "Let him cool his heels, Charles."

"I'd better go."

"No. I need your support—moral support. He's a tricky customer."

"Bolshy."

"Difficult to shift. That's why I took him on in the first place. I wanted someone who could stand up to the Press Barons and beat them."

"And now he's joined the barons and taken us on," Carpendale sighed. "I should have seen it coming. He was always complaining about one or other of us infringing his editorial freedom."

John was angry again. "It's not your fault he's gone in for muckraking and filth. I can smell the stink of it in this office. If anyone's to blame it's Ronald Norman. It's no good being Chairman and only being nice to everyone. Let's put our editor at his ease, facing the light. You sit here." He pointed at one of the easy chairs. "We'll make it a chat round the fire. Then we'll all shake hands and that'll be the end of Mr Lambert."

"Ah, but last time he thought he'd lost. This time he thinks he's won. He can afford to be magnanimous."

"What are you going to say to him?"

"I'll say what I think—same as I always do." He crossed to the door. "Come in Mr Lambert—sorry to keep you waiting."

Lambert seemed quite recovered from the ordeal which had almost shattered his health. "Good morning, Sir Charles," he said politely.

"Morning." The Admiral stood, legs apart, on the quarter-deck. As far as he was concerned, Lambert was a mutinous commander, but he tried not to show it.

"I hope you don't mind me collaring you before you've even got to the office," John continued. "But I go before the Cabinet Committee this afternoon, and I understand you're also giving evidence first."

"Yes."

"At midday." Lambert showed no. signs other than mild interest. "Well . . . sit down please."

Lambert took out an envelope from his breast pocket. "I brought you a copy of my review of *The Testament of Beauty*—

written according to your instructions." He proffered it to the Director General.

"I've read it, thank you." John didn't take it, aware that Lambert was trailing his coat.

"Did you like it, Sir John?"

"Not much. A poor effort." He never minced matters.

"I'm afraid Robert Bridges is hardly my favourite poet."

"I was with him the night before he died. He gave me a signed copy. I admired both him and his work enormously."

"Oh well, one man's meat . . . ." A faint smile hovered round the editor's lips.

"Quite so. Do sit down—here."

Lambert took the seat offered, facing the sunlight which slanted in through the windows. He made himself comfortable, surveying the room like a reporter seeking information. The family photographs, bowls of fresh flowers, the cheerful wood fire, neat pile of logs, and the homely drawing-room furnishings were hardly the habitat of a Nazi dictator. He disliked the man who so dominated his life but now that he'd won his case, he was prepared to negotiate a proper agreement which would ensure his future. In spite of the Director General's promises that he could start again *de nova*, he was painfully aware of hostility along the corridors. So long as he had been the injured party fighting injustice, he was surrounded by sympathetic friends. But now the pendulum had swung the other way. It was the Director General who was being pilloried.

Carpendale offered him a cigarette. "How did you get on on your holiday?"

"I went to Germany."

"Oh, I love Germany," said John. "Where did you go?"

"I was a guest at the Nuremberg Rally."

"Oh? I too was asked, but I refused."

"You should have gone. I met Hitler. Very friendly. He's done a great deal more for the working man than we have."

"From the point of view of adult education and the like?" John refused to be drawn into talk about Hitler. He'd recently had a long letter from Irene Wanner. He hadn't replied, but the contents had so disturbed him that he'd mentioned them to

Baldwin in person. "I believe adult education is your great hobby horse, isn't it?"

"Oh, I could go on about that for hours." Once again the faint mocking smile. "But you don't want to hear about that, you want to know what I'm going to say in front of the select committee, don't you?"

The sparring was over. John picked up the *Daily Express.* "Lambert, you've stirred up a hell of a lot of mud—and a lot of it's stuck. Not just to the B.B.C.—not just to me—to you as well." He paused. "What are you going to do about it?"

"Suppose you tell me."

John folded the paper over to reveal one of David Lowe's cartoons of himself being pursued by rats, and dropped it into Lambert's lap. "I don't mind being made a figure of fun, Lambert—in fact I quite like it—though I don't buy the originals like a politician. I like to regard myself as a hoarding round the B.B.C. If people throw rotten eggs at me, no matter—so long as the rest of the B.B.C. can carry on undisturbed. But when I get rotten eggs thrown at me by the very people I'm trying to protect—that breaks my heart."

Lambert passed the cartoon over to Carpendale, deliberately unmoved by the intensity with which John spoke. "What do you want me to say to the committee?"

"That's up to you—you're the first person to complain at an editorial interference!" That sunk home. "But I know what *I'm* going to say. The B.B.C. will not accept a new Charter limited to five years. I want another ten years—preferably twenty. I want no advertising. We must be independent like the Bank of England or the Royal Society. Why should we hand over fifty per cent of our licence fee to the Government, so they can give it back to us piecemeal or withhold it if they think we're naughty boys?"

Lambert smiled without the mockery. John had struck a chord.

He went on. "Do you know, Lambert, over the last seven years the Government has helped itself to eight millions of our money. Your money. All they need now is for you—a person well known as a man of integrity and ability and conscience—to give to the Cabinet Committee the sort of evidence you gave in your libel case. They'll pounce on it, Tory and Labour alike—and use it as an excuse to take over complete control of our finances, and thereby our policy, our programmes, and . . . our staff."

Lambert's eyes flickered towards Carpendale. He was nodding in agreement. He too was a member of the staff. "From that moment," John continued, "we will have to provide a service to the taste of Neville Chamberlain or Clement Attlee or whoever happens to be the umpteenth Post Master General. What sort of articles will they allow you to publish about Abyssinia or Spain or India . . . or the Nazis and the Jews?" He could see that Lambert was coming round to his point of view, but the editor still had the impassive regard of slight superiority. John got up and lit a cigarette. "You said you liked Hitler?" he remarked casually.

Lambert's answer was pedantic. "I believe he has a thirst for war, but a horror of starting one."

John nodded approvingly. "That's a very perceptive observation, isn't it, Sir Charles?"

"Yes, very." Carpendale wasn't sure what he was supposed to say. He knew John was about to spring the catch.

"When you met Adolph Hitler, did you also have a chance to meet Dr Goebbels?"

"Unfortunately no."

"Hm." John stroked his chin. "I think you met Dr Wanner, their director of Broadcasting on his last visit?"

"Yes, I believe I did."

"Because you might have asked Doctor Goebbels what happened to Dr Wanner, after he was ridiculed, and vilified, and finally beaten senseless?"

Lambert frowned. "I don't approve of the Nazis, God forbid."

"Yet you approve of Hitler and his thirst for war."

Lambert squirmed. "I've certainly no thirst for war—I'm a lifelong pacifist, like my father before me."

"And was his pacifism as aggressive as yours appears to be?"

"Well he campaigned actively as an M.P.—like his great friend Viscount Snowden."

As he expected, the mention of Snowden stopped the Director General like a bullet. "Snowden?" he repeated.

"Yes, he was my Godfather. I thought you knew." He looked up at John, and once again with a mocking smile.

"I know now," said John grimly. Then he smiled. It was a rare occurrence, and quite genuine. "But I won't hold it against you, provided his widow doesn't get herself back on the Board of Governors. Your job is secure Lambert—I give you my word."

It seemed to Carpendale that John had finally broken the ice. John thought so too, and became quite fatherly towards Lambert. "Now my advice to you is to go home and discuss what I've said with your wife—I hope she's better by the way—and . . . I was going to say 'Pray to God', but I seem to remember you saying you were an agnostic when I first met you."

"I still am. I'm a humanist."

"That means that at least you regard me as a human being." He smiled disarmingly.

Lambert responded almost eagerly. "Oh yes, Sir." And he jumped up almost like a schoolboy with his headmaster.

John regarded him from his great height. "In two hours' time you'll be standing alone in front of the Cabinet Committee representatives of this nation. Whatever you decide to do, you must know to be right—deep down within you." He took Lambert's hand and held it. "Otherwise you will have lost something which you don't believe in, but which I am utterly convinced is at the centre of every man's existence . . . You will have lost your soul."

Lambert looked into John's eyes. To his surprise he saw only genuine concern and sympathy. "Your soul," said John again and let go of Lambert's hand.

Lambert paused for a moment, and left the room in silence.

John went over to the window and looked out. He was remembering those arguments he'd had with Charlie, and how so often he'd won the day by the sheer intensity of his own convictions. Carpendale got up and stretched his legs too. He felt like a member of the audience who'd just watched a great actor whom he'd known and loved for many years, giving one of his great performances.

"He's an odd customer," he said. "But I doubt if he'll say anything against the B.B.C. from now on."

John turned quickly. "Oh, you think it worked, Charles, good!"

In a moment he had brushed the whole thing on one side, and after the Admiral had gone, he called in Jo Stanley and went through every detail of the case he was going to present to the Cabinet Committee. It would be an ordeal, but as long as he had no need to shuffle through papers and documents in order to answer the searching questions, he knew that he would retain the advantage. It would be "one against the lot of them", but one who was mentally and physically taller than any of them.

The Chairman joined John for lunch, and after it, the two men came down in the lift together. Ronald Norman behaved rather like an usher at a funeral, but John came out of the lift with the gleam of battle in his eyes. He was just crossing the hall when Mrs Bottle stepped forward. She'd evidently been waiting for him.

"Excuse me, Sir John, I've got something for you," and she held out an envelope. "I hadn't much time. I only saw the papers this morning. But we all thought we'd like to do something to show we don't agree with the House of Commons."

John opened the envelope. He was accustomed to Mrs Bottle as a disembodied voice putting calls through. He knew her well, and one glance at the contents of the envelope was enough to make him feel a glow of gratitude.

"Thank you, Mrs Bottle. Tell the staff I'm very grateful." He pushed the envelope into his pocket. "It's not only a testimonial, it's very useful ammunition."

To everyone's surprise he gave her a kiss on the cheek and walked out of the building en route for the Treasury.

There was no question of the Committee reaching a verdict—it sat in order to prepare a report on the recent conduct of the B.B.C.. But John was fully conscious that, however much notice they might take of other witnesses, the three-man Board conducted their business more like a Court Martial than anything else, and John was the man in the dock. The case for the B.B.C. would stand or fall by how he conducted his own case.

For three hours he stood answering their questions. By the time he'd finished, his sheer weight of knowledge and ability seemed to have satisfied his most severe critics. The Chairman began to sum up like a judge.

"Sir John, we appreciate very much the typical frankness with which you've spoken, and the cogent way in which you've presented your evidence. I'm sure you'll be relieved to know that we shall recommend that the terms of the new Charter be very much on the lines you suggest as far as financial control and general policy is concerned . . ."

John waited apprehensively for the "But" which he knew was coming.

"But . . . you still haven't answered the question as regards the rights of those who work within the B.B.C." He looked at the other members of the Board and they nodded back at him to show their foreknowledge of the body blow he was about to deliver. "Sir John, we've heard the same complaints on all sides—that there's no security of tenure . . . that it's all personal, interviews and bonuses and increments—salaries and promotion dependent on the whim of a few people . . . it's feudal serfdom. There appear to be no outlets for the natural feelings of frustration and anger which permeate the entire staff." He warmed to his theme. "If there's an injustice—and we all make mistakes—to whom can the unfortunate person appeal? None of us wants a repetition of the Lambert business now, do we?" He looked round at his colleagues and then back at John as though hoping he'd agree with him. John remained motionless. "I know what my answer to all this is," the Chairman came to the point at last". A Staff Association such as we have in most government departments . . . A Staff Association . . . What's your objection to that?"

There was a long pause. John slowly drew Mrs Bottle's envelope from his breast pocket. 'This is one of the rare occasions on which I'm going to allow my terrorised staff to speak for themselves." He walked over to the Chairman and gave him the envelope. "This was thrust in my hands just as I was leaving Broadcasting House. I knew nothing of it."

The Chairman studied the document he'd been presented with, then he read it out.

"We the undersigned, wish to express our loyalty to Sir John

Reith, and our entire approval of the way in which he conducts the affairs of all within the B.B.C.. We are happy to remain as we are, with the terms of our employment. We do not wish to be members of a Staff Association. Eight hundred signatures collected in two hours by Doreen Bottle."

He passed the document on to his colleagues.

"I gather it's the brainchild of one of our telephonists," said John helpfully.

There was a whispered consultation, then the Chairman said, "Well . . . that puts rather a different complexion on things. Of course there are still one or two minor reforms that we shall recommend, Sir John—we'll discuss them alone . . ." It was John's turn to nod approvingly. "But I don't think I'll be giving anything away when I say that this committee will certainly recommend that Sir John remains the Director General . . . " There were murmurs of approval. "Hopefully for another ten years."

"Ten years," thought John. "Hopefully I shall be in the Cabinet long before then!"

26

The ease with which he handled the three eminent parliamentarians fired John's political ambitions once more. He let it be known that he would consider favourably any approach from the Government, to help them out of their difficulties. Such hints as he dropped were usually accompanied by the wholehearted criticism of some high-ranking politician's policy, condemnation of his utter inadequacy, and a quick resumé of the steps that Sir John Reith would take to put things right, were he a member of the Cabinet, most of whom he public denounced as crooks or rats. He also caused unwitting offence by his assumption that the wives of politicians were unnecessary adjuncts. He couldn't understand why Mrs Chamberlain was expected to be treated with respect, for instance. His favourite story about her concerned her visit to Italy at the height of the Abyssinian crisis. Taking upon herself the role of unofficial mediator, she wired back to her husband a warning that he must impose sanctions immediately. "Now or Never—that's all she put!" John would relate with a chuckle. "Chamberlain took it to mean the moment had come for him to withdraw the Fleet! So Mussolini's got Abysinnia! It's not the first time Rome's been saved by a goose!" The only wife he approved of was Lady Willingdon, the wife of the Viceroy of India, and that only because he gave her the credit for raising a "nondescript greengrocer to be a peer of the realm and Viceroy of India"!

Most of his special likes and dislikes were reserved for Muriel's ears. As she never had a harsh word to say about anyone, she endured her husband's acidulated comments with stoic resignation. The advent of television—the world's first proper service—provided her with a welcome escape. Far from recognising it as the greatest advance in mass communication since wireless, John called it a waste of time and money. If a distinguished visitor displayed an interest, John would say, "Don't ask me—ask Baird, or Noel Ashbridge." Even so, as Director General he had to have a television set, and Muriel enjoyed watching it in spite of his disapproval.

"Why don't you read a book, Musie? This is a good read." He held his book up. *Crisis* by Winston Churchill.

Muriel wasn't impressed. "No, thank you." She didn't understand how John could dislike Churchill so much, and at the same time enjoy reading his book.

"I'll give it to Jean next time she comes."

Muriel continued to watch a programme in which Sir Malcolm Campbell talked about speed-boats. "Do you know Jean says Mother told her the Sutherland pictures were to go to her? She even says I can't have the rocking chair! I shall just go and take it! Robbery with violence if necessary."

Muriel was unmoved. John went over to her and bellowed in her ear. "Robbery with violence, do you hear?"

"I want to watch this. It'll be over in a minute."

"That's what I keep telling Ashbridge. It's a nine days wonder!" The telephone rang. "Phone!" He went over to switch the hated television off.

"Can't you take the call in the study?"

"No I can't. It could be the Prime Minister." He switched off the television and picked up the phone. "Reith here . . . Oh yes, sir." He whispered across to Muriel "It is the Prime Minister."

Muriel sat listening. She could hear Mr Baldwin talking, but only caught the odd word here and there. She guessed what it was. John had been preparing for several days for the announcements that would accompany the constitutional crisis should Edward refuse to give up his plans to marry a divorcee.

"No, no, everything's prepared, Prime Minister. You have only to say the word. I'll be in London in two hours time. I'll come and see you, sir . . . Goodbye."

John put the phone down. "As I thought—it's abdication! I'll stop at the Athenaeum till it's over."

He went up to the bedroom to put some things in a suitcase while Clark got the car out. Muriel followed him. "You mean the King's really going to . . .?"

"Yes! All for that wretched woman! What a pathetic man he is!"

On the night of December 10th, 1936, John stood outside the Augusta Tower at Windsor Castle. Next to him was a footman in scarlet uniform. They were waiting for the King, no longer King.

John was not one of those who sought to rub shoulders with Royalty. They added lustre to an occasion, and he enjoyed dressing up himself. He was quite happy to entertain them or be entertained, provided they kept their distance. His chief complaint against the Prince of Wales had always been his lack of dignity. It seemed wrong that the heir to the throne should be accorded all the privileges accorded to a royal broadcaster and finish up shaking hands all round and saying, "Thanks ever so—jolly nice." He was half afraid that King Edward VIII's abdication speech might turn out to be equally short and silly.

He found it odd that he should be deputed to stand on the doorstep of Windsor Castle to receive the owner, no longer owner. He decided to treat him quite naturally just as though he'd come to do a broadcast from Broadcasting House.

The royal headlights swept the dark archway and the car drew up in front of him. The footman opened the door. John remained at attention. First to alight was a small dog, then the King. He was smoking a cigar and wearing a fur coat over a light suit. John stepped forward, and the King shook hands. He seemed much as usual.

"Good evening, Reith—nice of you to come over yourself." He walked on past him.

John shook hands with Walter Monkton and followed them up the stairs. He found himself wondering what would become of the dog—it was a Cairn, he thought.

The broadcast had been arranged to take place in the King's private suite. John showed him where he would have to sit and suggested that he did a voice test. He felt like a surgeon instructing his patient before an operation. Professional calm. he gave the King a newspaper to read. It contained an article on sport, and John couldn't help admiring Edward's sense of humour as he read out an account of his own prowess as a tennis player.

"Quite complimentary, Reith."

He was such a likeable fellow. John was sorry for him, and suddenly thought of what the old King's secretary had said to him an hour or two earlier. "If only we could bump that woman off—but I can't do that myself, can I?" John was made of sterner stuff.

It was almost ten o'clock, so John sat at the microphone ready to make the announcement as soon as the red light came on. At that signal, he knew the ears of the whole world would be in that little room, and he thought proudly of the flawless efficiency of the organisation—the unseen engineers next door, the control room at Broadcasting House. He thought of his own family sitting at home, waiting for him to make this historic announcement.

"This is Windsor Castle. His Royal Highness the Prince Edward."

As he swopped places with the King, Edward gave the table a kick which Muriel said later sounded as if John had gone out, slamming the door in disgust! He tiptoed out of the room, sensing that the King would prefer to be alone when he made his last speech to the nation.

"At long last I am able to say a few words of my own. I have never wanted to withhold anything. But until now it has not been constitutionally possible for me to speak . . ."

John sat on an odd-shaped sofa in the King's bedroom, listening to his radio. Once again he knew himself to be at the heart of the nation—it was like Baldwin's speech on the General Strike ten years before. History was being made, and John Reith was there. It was not enough for him. He wanted to make history himself.

The King no longer King was speaking: "You all know the reason which has impelled me to renounce the throne. But I want you to understand that in making up my mind I did not forget the country or the Empire, which as Prince of Wales and lately as King, I have for 25 years tried to serve. But you must believe me when I tell you that I have found it impossible to carry the heavy responsibility and to discharge my duties as king as I would wish to do, without the help and support of the woman I love. And I want you to know that the decision I have made has been mine, and mine alone . . . "

"Help and support" . . .? She was going around saying he'd spoiled enough lives and she wasn't going to let him spoil hers! 'I'm going to get a nice fat sum out of him—King or no King!' That's what she says—that's the woman he loves!

It was too late for John to rush in and ban the banns.

The King saw him to the head of the stairs. "Thank you, Reith. I've always enjoyed making broadcasts with you in the past—I hope we may make others in the future."

John could only say, "I hope so too, sir." He bowed and shook hands and said "Good luck, sir." The King looked up at him and smiled. He seemed to be about to say something more and for a second John too felt that he wanted to say something—ought to say something—but he couldn't. He bowed his head again, and went home to Muriel.

He was very irritated to find that Lady Moir and some other neighbours were sitting up with Muriel, obviously waiting for him to return and tell them what had been going on. He ignored them and went straight to his study. He sat for a long time thinking what had just happened. Had it "just happened"? Had it been Edward's destiny all along to gain a crown, only to cast it on one side immediately. He thought of his own destiny too.

He heard Muriel's guests depart and she came to look for him. He told her everything.

"I cried," said Muriel. "I feel so sorry for the King."

"I feel sorry for his brother. Thrown in at the deep end. I was just sitting here thinking that perhaps I ought to offer him my services as Private Secretary."

Muriel smiled. "Director General of the B.B.C., and Private Secretary to the King?"

"What's so amusing about that?"

"Oh, darling, you are funny. How could you possibly . . .?"

"I'd resign as D.G. and become Chairman."

"Chairman?!" This was something Muriel had never heard before.

"Yes, when Norman's time is up."

"The Board would hate it."

"Hate to have His Majesty's Private Secretary as Chairman! They'd be on their knees in humble gratitude—they're all such snobs."

Muriel yawned. "Come on, let's go to bed."

"I need your help, Muriel, to clear my mind on this issue. I don't want to go on being Director General for another ten years. My mind needs stretching."

"What about the poor Duke of York. His mind'll need stretching with you for his secretary. He's got a stammer hasn't he?"

"What's that got to do with it? He'll need someone who knows the ropes and can organise his life for him."

"He's got a mother and a wife to do that."

"Och well, it was just one of my notions, as Mother used to say. Do you know, this is the first anniversary of her death." Muriel took his hand. "I miss her dreadfully. I pray to her every night. I ask God and Mother and Father to bring me through all the present critical and trying times. There are so many forces and individuals trying to overthrow me, Musie."

"They won't succeed, John. They're only the old rats gnawing at the foundations."

"Yes, you're right. And I suppose I should take comfort in the thought that the reason they all do it is because the worthier the building and the greater the achievement, the better obviously the feeding."

At least his problems were temporarily alleviated and he could cheerfully tell the King that in view of all the B.B.C. had done for the Coronation, he felt he should be allowed to offer up a golden microphone during the service.

The official banquets and meetings also brought him into close contact with the powers that be; and as everyone was striving for once towards the same objective, there was none of the usual animosity. After one such dinner he reported back to Carpendale: "I managed to have a word with Mrs Chamberlain's husband. Obstinate as a mule of course, but at least he's content to leave us alone."

"Will he leave us alone when he becomes Prime Minister though?" Baldwin intended to resign immediately after the Coronation.

"I shouldn't think so for a moment. But at least we'll have breathing space to find a new Director General."

"John!" The Admiral was completely taken aback.

"It won't be so much of an upheaval as you think. The Board will want to choose their own man of course, but when you resign I'll make Cecil Graves the Deputy Director General, so that all he'll have to do is step into my shoes, *Fait accompli.*"

"Are you asking for my resignation, John?" He didn't mind going at all, but he wasn't expecting to be told so abruptly. John seemed quite unaware of the Admiral's feelings.

"Yes," he said. "Now that the Charter's agreed—like I told you."

"What about you? Has Chamberlain offered you a place in his future Cabinet?"

"Alack no. He threw various sprats in my direction—like reorganising the defence of the realm."

"That's something you could do very well."

"Yes, I think so too." He was in fine spirits. "Whatever it is, I shall be fully stretched."

"But John, without you the B.B.C. will become just another government department. You bet your bottom dollar that's what Chamberlain's after."

"Charles, the B.B.C.'s not going to be without me. I shall be the next Chairman."

Carpendale looked at his friend. Did John really believe that Chamberlain would give him a Cabinet Office and the B.B.C. as well! "Chamberlain actually said that, did he?"

"Not in so many words—but he will."

Carpendale said nothing more. After all, he was only second-in-command, and soon wouldn't even be that.

The entertainment laid on by the Director General for his Deputy's departure might well have come straight out of *The Pirates of Penzance*—with the Admiral as the star of the show and John the actor manager. Just as Miss Nash had been made to

wave from the base of the funnel, so Carpendale had to mount
the platform in the Concert Hall in front of a capacity house of
staff, friends and relatives. He'd expected a small presentation in
the Board Room as a "send off".

John stood beside his friend and waited for the applause to die
down. "Admiral Sir Charles Carpendale came to the B.B.C. in
1924. I can picture him now—wrinkling his forehead in puzzle-
ment at the weird and wonderful people and things he'd
suddenly been called upon to deal with. But deal with them he
did, with characteristic gusty cheerfulness. His brilliant naval
career had given him a wider look at the world than was
vouchsafed to most of us. And his great gifts included an ability
to manage all sorts of men and situations with kindness and
firmness. Once upon his quarter-deck, even the most difficult
and cantankerous of people—such as musicians and Director
Generals—would agree to play together." There was applause as
the Concert Orchestra suddenly struck up a jazz accompaniment.
"The musicians have all given their services for the occasion, I
should add—an unparalleled tribute to a man who on one
occasion Sir Adrian Boult said should use one cello instead of
two, but play it twice as loud!" The laughter subsided and John
became serious. "Charles Carpendale was a friend to everyone at
the B.B.C., especially me. So when I say thank you and God
preserve you in all your doings and provide you with long and
happy retirement—when I present you with this tribute from all
of us here at the B.B.C. who've known and loved you—I say it
from the heart—'Thank you, Admiral'."

Carpendale took the couple of seascapes John had bought for
him out of the money collected, and held them up for all to see.
"The great feature of Sir John's leadership is that you know
where you are with him—there's no tittle-tattle. He's made it
quite clear to me and everyone else that I have now retired!"

The Admiral addressed the ship's company. He looked
deliberately towards members of the Board of Governors—
officers new to the ship like Mallon and Sir Ian Fraser—
challenging their loyalty. "Now I'm glad to see there are still lots
of familiar faces from the Savoy Hill days, and their owners will
admit that when we're together, we sometimes flatter each other

that we've played a prominent part in making the B.B.C. what it
is. But it was not any one of us who made the B.B.C., it was the
B.B.C. who made every one of us! . . . And Sir John Reith made
the B.B.C.. Thank you, Sir John."

John shook his hand. The Admiral's eyes were moist. "Three
Cheers for the Admiral—Hip, Hip, Hooray!"

The audience responded lustily and the band struck up a few
bars of *Rule Britannia*. John held up his hand—a signal for
silence and for a contingent from the Navy to march onstage.

"He'll now be piped over the side!"

The ex-Deputy Director smiled and waved and walked towards the sailors. Suddenly he realised that they were real
sailors, really piping him over the side. Automatically he came to
attention and saluted—then the band struck up and he walked
down the steps of the stage and out of the concert hall,
surrounded by well-wishers.

John stopped clapping. He remained at the side of the stage,
watching Carpendale—no pain of parting, retired almost before
he knew it had happened. He wondered how he'd feel when it
was his turn to go.

27

Cecil Graves succeeded Carpendale as Deputy Director General. The appointment wasn't opposed by the Board of Governors, but there were those who, like Sir Ian Fraser, were against Reith almost on principle, and regarded Graves as being no more than the "graven image" of the Director General he cordially disliked. John thought the "blind hero" traded on his affliction, and was bored with him showing off. Fraser memorised the agenda, and the documents under discussion, and took a delight in tripping people up. He also knew considerably more about the beginnings of wireless than John did, having been a radio ham before the war, but used his position as a governor to get himself special treatment at the Cenotaph. Such behaviour was anathema to John, and his dislike of Fraser was not in the least cordial.

Another Board meeting dragged on into the afternoon. Mallon said, "I'd like to put in the minutes that there is insufficient coordination between one department and another. And I emphasise the word 'coordination'."

Mallon had kept them all waiting for over an hour, so John was more than usually irritated. "In my opinion, 'coordination' is a monstrous word implying inefficiency."

"In that case let me rephrase. Let me say that there should be greater rationalisation of programme planning—will that do?"

"Rationalisation simply means something is wrong—that's all."

"What shall I put in the minutes?" Miss Stanley asked.

"You sort it out, Miss Stanley, we can't." Ronald Norman was anxious to get on, and his bland humour was a valuable contribution to his Chairmanship. "I think we should consider the list of possibilities for the post of Director General—have you got it, Sir John?"

"Miss Stanley's written them all out with their case histories. Will you give them out Miss Stanley? They're all numbered, and I may add 'Top Secret' and have to be signed for."

There was a buzz of interest round the table. John had been threatening to resign for years, but this was the first time that the question of who was to take his place had been seriously considered. It had resulted from a previous meeting at which John had hinted that he might be the next Ambassador in Washington. Fraser had immediately taken him up on it, and demanded that something be done, otherwise they'd only have one string to their bow—Cecil Graves.

He now said, "I don't need a list of names, thank you Miss Stanley. As far as I'm concerned there's only one possibility— Professor Ogilvie."

"Your concern should be for the B.B.C., not the Conservative Party."

"I'll treat that remark with the contempt it deserves."

"If we're to resort to clichés, I'll say I'm a man who calls a spade a spade and leave it at that."

The Chairman intervened. "I don't really think we should get all worked up about this at the moment. This is all purely speculation. Sir John hasn't even resigned yet, and I for one would much prefer him to stay."

Lady Bridgeman said, "Hear, hear", but there was silence from the others.

For John it was a wearying repetition of the old squabbles which had sapped his energies before. He couldn't go on indefinitely like this. The Prime Minister and everybody else knew he was looking for another job. If he didn't hear something very soon, he'd go and see the Prime Minister himself.

Muriel and John's friends could see the dangerous signs of the return of the accidie—bitterness and disillusion, self-analysis and recrimination: "It's all humbug and hypocrisy—I haven't done two hours real work all week!"

He spent more and more of his spare time taking Helen Moir to the theatre and amateur theatricals. The B.B.C. had an extremely

professional company, and John's performances were seen at the
Fortune Theatre by a mass of newspaper critics eager to draw
blood. But they stayed to cheer a natural actor, and moreover one
who could make an audience laugh uproariously. John loved the
experience of being once again part of a team, of sharing and
suffering as an equal, and of being acclaimed without hesitation
or reservations as the best in the team. He who'd been too tall for
the scrum, and too "difficult" to be head boy or even top of the
class, could feel what Wordsworth had felt: "Bliss was it in that
dawn to be alive, But to be young was very heaven."

The summer passed and winter came, and still no summons
from Downing Street, only second-hand gossip from Chequers
parties. Apart from his excursions into the West End—and
theatre-going had been a lifelong habit with him in any case—
John crept home early from the office, driven by Jo Stanley in
her Austin Seven.

"This is a terrible car."

"Yes, but you're always glad of a lift," remarked his secretary.
And it was true that he much preferred to sit hunched up in the
Austin with Jo than take the Buick driven by Mansbridge.

Being at home wasn't as it used to be either. He and Jo Stanley
would spend hours doing the diaries or pasting up the scrapbooks. He worked on an edition of his war diaries for publica-
tion, burned old letters, cleared out the stables when Muriel
wasn't around. He couldn't bear "rubbish" as he called the bits
and pieces of furniture that Muriel had stored away.

"Give it to the Naylors," was his battle-cry. They and other
relatives would drive home after a visit, unaware that he'd filled
the boot with bits and pieces or stuffed books between the folds
of the hood.

Hens were counted and recounted. Egg graphs multiplied, the
pond stocked with fish.

"There's nothing for the children to do here during the
holidays," Muriel complained.

"They can fish." He bought a boat, and that was the end of that.

Once the Admiral of the Fleet invited him to come on some
naval exercise. Muriel pressed John to go. He consented, but
only after he'd taken a night class in navigation. Once a week he

set out from home to High Wycombe, and along with working men out to better themselves, he learned how to steer by the stars. After he'd been there for a time, one of his mates asked him who he worked for.

"The B.B.C."

"Are you his butler?" the man asked, looking at John's pinstripe trousers. John didn't disillusion him, and was very sorry when the man said one day, "I know who you are, Sir John Reith." There was an element of Lawrence of Arabia about his conduct. John knew that. He could understand Lawrence wanting to remain as an unknown soldier. John would have liked to have gone back to those days. He hated his office on top of the B.B.C. sometimes. He dined out whenever he could, preferring to meet people at their offices. Anything to avoid the pervasive illness which seemed to be taking hold of him.

"I must do something. The world needs me. A war's coming. I could prevent it. If only Chamberlain would offer me something. Lloyd George said he'd have been able to solve the unemployment problem with me!"

The call didn't come, and John went off to the local Territorial Hall and stood in line with other volunteers and gave his name. Then he went off to dinner with the Chancellor of the Exchequer and told him what he'd done.

"I think we can find you something better than that," said the Chancellor. But he didn't.

John went to sea with the Fleet and sat over dinner surrounded by Admirals and statesmen hanging on his every word. He went up on the bridge, and he heard the captain of the battleship announce to the Fleet, "Sir John Reith is at the helm." He was indeed. He felt the power and might of Britain in his hands. He could have been commander of a battleship and all his dreams would have been fulfilled.

When he went down to his cabin he was lost and lonely. He remembered how on the cruise he'd had a cable from Muriel. C.J. had been rushed to hospital with appendicitis. John had been sitting at the Captain's table surrounded by the rich and famous. He'd felt as though he'd been kicked in the stomach. He'd left the table and gone down to his cabin and knelt beside his bunk and prayed to God to save C.J. With tears streaming down his cheeks, he'd dedicated his life to God if only He'd save C.J.

Muriel was at Portsmouth to greet him on his return from his naval engagement. She drove him home via Christopher's prep school.

"He's homesick," said Muriel.

"Can't be. He's only been there a month."

"The first time at a new school's the worst."

"The last's far worse. Don't worry, he'll soon make friends. That's what I always say about C.J. He may be brainless, but he's very friendly."

"How can you call your own son brainless?"

"Well, look at that microscope Mrs Clarke gave him for Christmas. Not interested. Marista could hardly keep her hands off it."

"That's because she's jealous."

"Marista jealous?" Nothing was bad enough for Christopher or good enough for Marista. "Jealous? Rubbish. I can talk to her, but C.J. is like talking to a brick wall. All he wants to do is feed the hens and cut up logs."

"Only because he admires you, John, and wants to be like you, and that's the only thing he ever sees you do when you're at home."

"Poor old C.J." Such a thought had never occurred to him. He was contrite. "I'm not much of a father."

They drove on in silence. Then John said "Homesick . . . Got too much soul, that's his trouble. I'll have a word with the Headmaster and see if he can part with him for a weekend." Muriel was pleased. "Cheer him up."

A fortnight later, John came in for his tea. He'd heard the gong, but he'd been busily having one of his clear-outs, and forgotten that Christopher was bringing a friend home for the weekend. "I told you he'd soon make friends, Musie."

Muriel had gone to a lot of trouble to see that Christopher had all his favourites on the table, and he was tucking in with even more than his usual relish. John took his seat at the head of the table and watched him. Obviously manners were not a high priority at Sandroyd, though his friend seemed much more dainty in his habits.

"I can see everything you've got in your mouth, Christopher. Don't make it worse by clapping your lips."

"I'm not."

" 'Eat nice,' as Winnie says."

Muriel frowned across at him. Why had John to be such a dampener at the feast?

Christopher licked his fingers and took another cake. John clicked his tongue "And don't . . . Here, what's a paper napkin for?" He thrust one at him.

"Don't go on at him, John," said Muriel. "You're spoiling his day."

"If he'd been taught manners instead of romping about in the nursery . . ."

"Oh please, John."

John turned his attention to the friend. He hadn't taken notice of him before. He was taller than Christopher and a good-looking lad.

"Have another scone . . . er . . . MacTavish."

"I'm not MacTavish," said the boy.

"Well. I've got to call you something—what's wrong with MacTavish?" The boy was amused. "You see what happens if you don't introduce people, Christopher? They get called MacTavish."

Why was Muriel looking at him like that?

The boy giggled. "My name's Charles."

"Charles What?"

"Bowser."

"Bowser." He contemplated C.J.'s friend. "Now we have it— Charles Bowser. You must be from Scotland. What a coincidence.." He looked across at Muriel. She was smiling at him. "Is your father called Bowser too?"

"Yes, sir."

The cross-examination was at an end. Muriel breathed again. "Now what about jelly and ice cream?" She helped the boys.

John got up. "So this is your plot, Muriel?"

"Plot?"

"Shirley Temple and the 'Little Colonel'? 'Little Lord Fauntleroy', eh? Bearing the olive branch." Muriel sat frozen. She knew all the signs. It was only a question of seconds before the storm would break.

"How long have you been at Sandroyd, Charles?"

"Two years, sir."

"Two years." He spoke to Muriel. "And you chose the school, Muriel." She looked down at her plate. "Charles, did you know that your father and I were acquainted? You look not unlike him—has anyone ever told you that before?"

"Oh, yes," said the boy enjoying his trifle. "My old man says I'm the spitting image."

"Spitting image, is that so." He surveyed the boy for a moment, then said abruptly. "Why don't you take your friend in the garden, Christopher?"

"It's freezing outside."

"The nursery then!" There was rage in John's voice which flabbergasted the boy. "Go up to the nursery!"

Christopher took a last cake. He wasn't going to let his father spoil his tea.

"Play ping-pong," Muriel suggested. "Go on, I'll take on the winner."

The boys left the room together. Glad to escape. Muriel waited patiently.

"Of all the despicable things to do."

"Charlie and Maisie are my friends."

"You've been conducting a secret correspondence."

"Secret? Of course not. We've had Christmas cards and the one after your mother died."

"Don't lie!" John was almost beside himself. "There can be no trust or happiness if there are lies! Speak the truth!"

Winnie came in to clear away. She looked pale and miserable. She'd not been well for months. "It's all right, Winnie," said Muriel. "Go to bed early. I'll manage."

"Thank you, my lady. Did you have a pleasant day?"

"Yes, thank you, Winnie."

"No we did not, Winnie. Take some syrup of figs—there's some in the bathroom cupboard."

Winnie retired gratefully. She was glad she'd be able to go upstairs and shut the door and not have to listen to the two of them quarrelling. She hated it when it happened. She was so much part of the family.

As she closed the door she heard John say: "Go on, I'm listening, if there's anything worth listening to."

John stood looking out of the window. Muriel continued to sit at the table, surrounded by the boys' tea-party. "John," she said quietly. "Have you ever asked yourself why you and Charlie were friends in the first place?"

"Never. We weren't friends. We were David and Jonathan. Brothers—till Jezebel came along."

"Maisie. You pushed her into his arms and pushed him into hers. You arranged the wedding and fixed up the honeymoon and signed the register. And when it was all over you expected Charlie to come back and say, 'Thank you for my wife and family and now I am yours for ever and ever.' You're always going on about the virtues of loyalty, but you wouldn't let him be loyal to Maisie."

"Muriel, I offered Charlie a job. He could have been in the B.B.C.—at my side—from the very beginning."

"He had to get away from you, John. Like a son getting away from his father. You can understand that? Didn't you want to get away from your father?"

"Never. Charlie refused my offer. He rejected me."

He went out, closing the door behind him as though to stop Muriel following him, and she heard him go to his study.

She cleared the tea things and then went up to the nursery. John didn't re-emerge till after the boys had gone to bed. He'd had no supper. Muriel sat knitting in the drawing room. At last she heard the study door open and John went to the lavatory. He returned to the study and came into the drawing room a moment later, carrying a letter he'd written.

"Muriel, I will now read you my letter to Charlie. I've added a postscript—I'll read that first." His voice was level and un-emotional. It frightened Muriel. She'd never heard him like that. It was as though every emotion had been drained from him. "I didn't know a child of yours was at Sandroyd till this afternoon.

If in future any of us chance to meet there (or anywhere else for that matter) let it be as strangers." He turned the page over and continued without even glancing at Muriel.
"Dear Mr Bowser,
Recently I came across a copy of a letter from my late mother to you, and your reply." One of his clear-outs, thought Muriel, and almost smiled. "She made some quite inaccurate, unfounded and incredible remarks which even this late I want to correct. She wrote that I still:
1) Had photos of you in evidence.
2) Felt friendly towards you and regretted the termination of our acquaintance.
3) Desire its resumption.
     I cannot imagine where she got all this nonsense from."
     Muriel looked down at her knitting. He was tormenting her and himself at the same time. Surely he must realise that his mother loved him and wanted his happiness and hoped that perhaps Charlie might bring some of it back?
     John went on with his letter. "There hasn't been a photo or relic of you in my possession for years. A ring was sold for its gold equivalent. The prayer book you gave me at the top of the Cairngorms, long since lost."
     How could he write that to Charlie, as though he'd never thought of him? When he went through the diaries with Jo Stanley, he kept all that he'd written about Charlie. He'd kept all his letters and re-read them, and only burned them a few years ago.
     "You say you are ever on the look out for a bridge and that if you ever find it, you trust you will have the strength to cross it. . . ." Muriel looked up and stared at him. He wasn't reading from the letter. He knew it by heart. "Whatever do you mean by that Charlie? Anything at all? No reply required. Yours Truly."
     He folded the letter carefully and put it in an envelope and sealed it. Then he said to Muriel in quite his normal voice. "I'm sorry you don't approve."
     Muriel shook her head in disbelief. "After meeting his son? A little boy? How could you feel so bitter and resentful? Don't you need friendship and love? Don't you want it any more? To write

a letter like that!"

John got up from his chair. "Those young days are dead. This letter buries them."

He walked out of the room to the pillar box down the lane.

Muriel sat with her knitting clutched in her hands.

28

By cutting Charlie finally out of his life, John felt he had cauterised the wound which for so many years had sapped his personal relationships. He'd demonstrated to Muriel that there was now no one else but her and the children. Yet he was no happier, because the life he'd built for himself at the B.B.C. was crumbling away.

At the same time as he bought Muriel a new electric sewing machine and exchanged the Buick for a Wolseley, he refurnished the office and got rid of his old chair. Would that make life different? Muriel preferred the Buick.

Why should he spend hours listening to Sir Ian Fraser demanding that the new Charter should actually include—in writing—details such as that the agenda should be sent out a week before the Board met?

"He's on the make—a political ramp!"

"Well he *is* blind, John." Muriel could just imagine what John would be like if he were sightless.

"That doesn't give him the right to keep droning on through meetings. He's also rather stupid."

"Can't you forget about him and just talk to the other governors?"

"He's still there! You remember how Mrs Hamilton said 'I don't want to sit next to that man'? She felt the same as me."

"Can't you have a word with Ronald Norman?"

"What's the good of that? He agreed with Mallon that the governors should each have a special area of interest—be 'departmentalised' is how he put it! He took frightful umbrage when I tactfully suggested that it was a ridiculous thing to do, but he could take an interest in the stuff if he'd nothing to do! Snowden and the White Rabbit all over again. The Governors are an infernal nuisance!"

He went into his study and had another go at Christopher's jigsaw puzzle. It took him till after midnight to finish it.

Before he knew it, Christmas was there again—White Christmas and he might as well be in the Black Hole. No sign of a new job worthy of his abilities. He lay on his back in the study, suffering from lumbago. And he did so want to be outside with the children, throwing snowballs and the sun gleaming over a white world. If a war came his children would suffer because he'd failed to prevent it. He'd been too busy working on the report on "Accents"!

He rolled over and studied the pattern of the carpet. He hadn't looked so closely at it since he and Jean used to play tiddley-winks on it in his father's study. She'd sent her usual card and book tokens for the children, with a long letter about money. He could hear Marista and Christopher with their Christmas party playing on the stairs. He got up painfully—his lumbago was a bit better. A note to ring Adrian Boult on his desk—what a weird man—spending Christmas worrying about accepting a knighthood because Myra Hess had only got the C.B.E. for doing "twice as much as I have"! John phoned him up. "Adrian, I recommended you, and I wouldn't have done if I hadn't thought you deserved the honour. Take it on behalf of all the other great musicians if you like. Happy Christmas!" That'll settle his hash.

The noise on the stairs was deafening. He got all the children up in the nursery and they had a sing-song round the piano. Gradually the clouds cleared from his mind, and after the other children had gone, the family sat together in the drawing room and listened to the wireless and roasted chestnuts on the fire. He decided quite definitely that he would go and see the Prime Minister and ask for a job. That night he collected up four dozen of the children's Christmas cards and put them in their scrapbook—to please them.

On Boxing Day he found a small chicken dying, and he and Christopher forced some brandy down it and wrapped it up in cotton wool and put it by the fire, and by some miracle—it lived.

1938 and Munich lay ahead.

The Prime Minister was off to see Hitler when John finally
caught up with him. Like a man who is packing his suitcase, he
wasn't prepared to sit down and pass the time of day. He had the
highest regard—knew of no one with a higher claim—would
ensure his brilliant abilities were not wasted. . . . As John saw
him off in his car outside Number 10, the Prime Minister said, "I
wish you were coming with me."

"I wish I was too, sir." Hitler was poised to invade Austria, and
what would Chamberlain do about that? Britain had nothing to
stop him, a weak country run by a weak and obstinate man who
didn't think it worth his while to find a place in his Government
for a leader who would get things moving. John knew he had it
in him—he wished he could have the power of a benevolent
dictator. He'd use it to the glory of God!

He walked back to the B.B.C. The main hall was soon to be
given a mild dressing of sandbags. On his desk was a letter from
the Ministry of Defence. What was he intending to do if a bomb
dropped on Broadcasting House? He dictated a reply:
"Dear Sir,

    With regards the . . . Does it matter?
                    Yours etc."
The lunacy of it all. He thought he was going to reorganise the
War Office at one time—he was still at the B.B.C., and the War
Office still as disorganised.

He took the 3.30 home and found that Muriel had gone
shopping. He sat in his study for a moment. Clark came past the
window. He called to him: "Clark, will you come in here a
moment—I want to do a bit of reorganising."

Clark helped John carry his desk across to the window. Then
they rearranged the books.

"That's much better," said John. "Now I can see what I'm
doing. Now let's put the diaries next to the scrapbooks—all of a
piece. That's more like it, isn't it?"

"Till the next time." Clark was accustomed to his master's
vagaries.

"Change is good for the soul," John remarked.

"Oh, is that what it's for?"

"Och yes. Here, take these books for Mrs Clark. Can she do much reading?" She'd been ill.

"Not a lot. But she'll appreciate them, I know."

"Tell her I recommend Kitchener's biography—quite racy."

When Muriel came in with Marista, she found John writing a letter. He was seated by the window in the new position. The wastepaper basket was on the desk in front of him, and peering out of it Timmy the cat. Marista picked the cat up and carried him off to the kitchen.

"Been shopping?" asked John.

"Not really. I saw the doctor, the dentist, the oculist and the chiropodist."

"So you're like the Wolseley—fully serviced? I'm just writing to Irene Wanner. I had another letter from her this morning— pathetic. She's left home—doesn't know what to do."

"How's her father?"

"In her first letter she said he wouldn't have anything more to do with her—now she doesn't even mention him. She wants to come over. She's probably a member of the Hitler Youth. I'll give her what advice I can, and make it clear that I don't want anything more to do with her."

Muriel knew it was useless for her to protest that Irene must need his help very badly to have written twice. She'd trans- gressed by getting married, and must be cut off. "You've changed the room round."

"Yes. A great improvement, don't you think? I can get the sun on my back, and the diaries and scrapbooks are all together." He went over to the bookcase, avoiding the question which was uppermost in both their minds.

"So the Prime Minister didn't offer you anything?" Muriel knew already.

"He said I was a genius, but he did not offer me a Cabinet post." He opened one of the scrapbooks. "Scrapbook for 1926. We ought to have a plaque on the desk. 'At this desk Stanley Baldwin made the broadcast which broke the General Strike'. Remember that?" He closed the book and put it back on the shelf. "I suppose I'm what's called 'bitterly disappointed'."

"That's why you changed the furniture around?"

"No, no,—it's to get the sun." He didn't sound very convincing. "Chamberlain wants me to reorganise, revitalise, reunite the airways of the country."

Muriel picked her words carefully. "That sounds like . . . a challenge."

"Challenge!" John came out with it at last. "To reorganise British Airways a challenge! I should have a Ministry. I nearly walked straight out—damned shilly shallying—Germany's on the march! When I'm challenged I put a favour in my cap and hold my lance aloft and charge the enemy!"

"And wear your heart on your sleeve." He looked comical in his Worshipful Archers hat that he wore to keep his head warm.

"When it comes to politics, I'm unsentimental and unemotional."

"So you didn't accept?"

"I said I was reluctant—very reluctant."

"Why?"

"Various reasons. Among other things I told him you don't like flying—hate it."

Muriel was incensed. "That's got nothing to do with it."

"You're my wife. You're a very important part of my life. And if you don't like what I'm doing, I can't be happy."

This was news to Muriel. "But you need a change, John, a job like this will stretch you."

"Only if I can work at the B.B.C. at the same time. Otherwise—I told him—I shall feel castrated. Constipated and castrated were my actual words."

"But you can't possibly be Director General and at the same time . . ."

John cut her short, rubbing his hands together in his sudden agitation. "I can be Chairman! Norman's time is up—I can be Chairman. Cecil Graves can be Director General and I can be Chairman!"

"You told the Prime Minister that?" She could see it all now.

"No. I shall tell him after the Governors' meeting next week. Once they understand the situation they'll be thrilled to bits." He looked straight into Muriel's eyes—read her disbelief—ignored what he read. "Only Ian Fraser wants me to go—Norman said so. The others know that to have me as the next Chairman will solve a lot of problems."

There was a silence, like a gulf opening between them.

The Governors' meeting passed without John revealing his true intentions. The names of candidates for Director General were deliberated upon along with other business, yet there was an air of unreality about it all. John had not yet resigned, and whenever he spoke to a member of the Board alone, the tenor of the conversation was always the same. "You mustn't resign. It's vital that you stay. We need you more than ever." If that was the message carried back to Number 10, why was Chamberlain asking him to leave? It'd be different if John were needed in the Cabinet, but he wasn't.

The more he had to do with British Airways, the less he liked it. Was he supposed to join the cabal of people like Horace Wilson, the P.M.'s Secretary, and the hated crook, Kingsley Wood, in order to get rid of Wood Humphrey the man he was supposed to supplant? They'd been apprentices at the locomotive plant thirty years ago—he wasn't going to go behind his back. Not that he thought Wood Humphrey any use—he'd made a mess of the job—but John's loyalty to the old days wouldn't permit treachery.

He spent most of his time outside the office. He saw little of Muriel and more of Helen Moir—though Marista played there all one afternoon while Muriel went shopping. Miss Stanley entertained her with jigsaw puzzles, and they had fun with the "Ant's Palace"—sent by the head of N.B.C. John liked to watch the ants running around the corridors with their eggs—like Whitehall bureaucrats with their endless memorandums.

June came in. Hitler had collared Austria without a word of protest. No word from the Wanners. Events at the B.B.C. moved slowly towards the choice of a successor. John returned to Downing Street to see Horace Wilson. Still nothing new to suggest. He went back to the B.B.C. His mind was made up. He would tell the Board what he wanted them to do and they would do it as they always had in the past.

29

John certainly didn't expect the Governors to accept their orders without demur, but he was not at all prepared for the stony silence which ensued after he'd finally put all his cards on the table. Norman spoke eventually—looking at his fellow members, almost as if John had left the room.

"In a nutshell, what Sir John is suggesting is that we appoint Cecil Graves as Director General, so that Sir John can take on the job of Chairman of Imperial Airways." He turned to John "You want us to recommend that you become the next Chairman of the B.B.C.?"

"The Prime Minister's anxious that you make your decision known as soon as possible." He tilted his chair back and clasped his hands behind his head.

"We'll do our best," said Norman. "But it's very short notice."

"Oh, you've known for years I was wanting to leave!" He smiled round.

"Wanting to leave—yes. But not wanting to be Chairman."

John sat up. What was this?

Miss Fry spoke kindly, as though he were a patient with some unfortunate disease. "Sir John, we all love you dearly, but we can't rush this through. After all, we've agreed to see Professor Oglivie the day after tomorrow."

"Och aye. If you seriously want a Director General who doesn't know the first thing about broadcasting and wouldn't say boo to a goose . . ." He refused to take her seriously.

"Now, now, let's be fair," said Norman, feeling that he was no longer in control of the situation.

"Yes, be fair. Ring him up and tell him not to come and we'll refund his train fare. Say you're very sorry but you'd rather have the devil you know. You couldn't get a better Director General than Grave . . . Or a better Chairman than me," he added with a laugh.

The stony silence was now icy.

"John," said Miss Fry gently. "I think the feeling of the Board is that we'd prefer to discuss this alone."

"Very well." He turned to Jo Stanley. "Miss Stanley, do you mind . . . ?

She gathered up her papers. Fraser spoke harshly. "Miss Fry means without you."

Miss Stanley stopped. She'd almost reached the door. She looked back. John rose slowly to his feet. His face was expressionless. "Right, gentlemen," he said. "I'll be in my office."

Nobody made any attempt to stop him leaving the room. Jo Stanley followed him out, and by the time she got to the office, the Director General's door was closed.

She knocked on the door and entered.

John was standing by the window, looking out. He didn't turn round. "Let me know when the Board is ready to receive me, Miss Stanley."

"Yes, sir." She hesitated to leave. His voice sounded strange. "Yes, Sir John." She went out.

John heard the door close. From his window he could see two of the announcers crossing the road. One of them was Woodruffe. Leaving early for a drink, no doubt. One of Lobby's protégés. His commentary had made history—the Spithead Review—"Special Report from the Vanguard. The Fleet's lit up! The Fleet's lit up!" He'd sat him on a chair in the Board Room, heard the evidence, and put the fear of God into him. And that was the end of the matter. He quite liked the fellow. If Lobby'd only come to him he could have told him: "Don't let him anywhere near the Navy—he's got a drink problem!"

He sat down at his desk and picked up the phone. "Mrs Bottle, put me a call through to the Prime Minister please."

He put the phone down and waited for it to ring again. He tried to sit outside himself and view the situation dispassionately. By sending him out of the room, the Board had behaved as though he were a candidate for the job, not the holder. In spite of all his experience they had preferred to choose his successor without his guidance. He brought his fist down on his desk with a thump—it could mean only one thing—"They are not going to ask me to stay on as Director General—they don't want me to be Chairman. I can't force myself on them—unless I am the Prime Minister's nominee."

The phone rang. John picked it up. He heard Mrs Bottle say, "Your call to Downing Street, Sir John."

"Reith here."

It was Sir Horace Wilson. "The Prime Minister will have a word with you, Sir John. He's rather busy."

"Thank you." He took the hint.

"Yes, Sir John, what can I do for you?"

"I won't waste your time. Prime Minister, sir, am I instructed by you to join Imperial Airways?"

He heard Chamberlain give a faint cough. "I wouldn't say instructed exactly."

John reassured him. "I don't mind being instructed. I'm not a Civil Servant, but I'm prepared to do what I'm told."

"Oh, I know how cooperative you are, Sir John."

Liar. "My Board wants a decision and so do I. Do you or do you not want me to go?"

"Oh, I don't want to order you to do anything you may regret. I shall get blamed."

"I'm not trying to make you say something of which I can take advantage later." John was being very patient.

"No, no, I'm sure you're not." The Prime Minister was falling over backwards to be kind. When would he stick the knife in? "But from my own point of view—I don't want to do something to you, for which I may chide myself later."

John became exasperated. "Prime Minister, you are the leader of the Government—as such you are its spokesman—quite impersonal. Is it the wish of His Majesty's Government that I should join Imperial Airways?" Let him try to squirm out of that one!

"Yes, Sir John. That is the wish of the Government."

John took a breath. "Thank you, sir. Then I accept the job."

"Excellent. I'm very pleased." He seemed to think the conversation was at an end.

"One moment, Prime Minister." This was the question that he dreaded asking, that he had to ask. "Is it also the wish of the Government that I go from the B.B.C.?" There was a long silence. "Prime Minister?"

"That is the Government's desire—yes."

John held on to the phone, like a driver frozen to the wheel. "That's all I wanted to know. It's the first thing the Chairman of the B.B.C. will ask me—whether you told me myself . . ." He felt he was burbling. "It's the first thing my wife will ask me . . ."

"Yes, I'm sure."

"Thank you, Prime Minister. I hope I shall prove a loyal and . . ."

He heard the phone click at the other end. He couldn't have gone on anyway. It was as though he'd been hit in the face.

He remembered walking home from school one evening—past the cricket nets. A straight drive over the bowler's head had struck him . . .

So this was the end. "It is the Government's desire—I must go from the B.B.C."

He put his head in his hands—it was bursting. The singing noise in his ears was deafening . . . A cricket ball—was that the explanation? No. There were tears in his eyes. He felt them on his cheeks. He was back in the trenches. It wasn't a cricket ball— it was a bullet. He'd been hit in the face—a bullet in the head. Blood everywhere—his new tunic ruined. Blood everywhere. He shouted out. "The bullet's in my head, the bullet's in my head— my tunic's ruined!"

"Sir John—Sir John. Hullo, hullo!" The receiver was still in his hand. Mrs Bottle was calling him. "Have you finished, Sir John?"

"Oh? Yes, yes, thank you." He was about to replace the receiver. "Oh, Mrs Bottle?"

"Yes, Sir John?"

"How many calls of mine do you think you've put through?"

"Today?"

"No. Since the first one . . . At Magnet House."

"Oh . . ." She sounded puzzled. "I don't know. Thousands I

should think."

"Thousands. At any rate, Mrs Bottle, I've probably spoken to you more than to any other woman—and never a cross word. That's all."

He replaced the receiver. The bullet hadn't killed him. Smashed his teeth, spoiled his looks and ruined his new uniform—but it hadn't been the end of him. He'd written to Mother: "I'm all right—John." He'd written to Charlie: "Cheer up, Dear Old Boy." Charlie'd come to see him in hospital when they'd done the dressing. It had been a most terrible shock for him. Poor Charlie. But it wasn't the end.

He got up and went over to the office door.

"Miss Stanley, I want to dictate."

Jo Stanley came in with her pad, and seated herself in front of the desk as she always did—pencil poised.

John walked up and down as he always did.

"To whom it may concern.

When this reaches you I shall have left the B.B.C." He heard Jo Stanley's involuntary, "Sir John". He didn't look at her. "It is not possible to take leave even of heads of departments individually, but the mere going is painful enough so I am not altogether sorry. I cannot leave, however, without sending this note to wish you and your staff every happiness and good fortune. If your work and personal contacts bring you as much satisfaction as mine have me, you will realise when your time comes, how I am feeling today. Goodbye and thank you."

Jo got up. She was afraid she might cry. John was over by the window, looking out, his back to her. "See that it's on the desks of all section and departmental heads first thing in the morning. Nobody's to see it till then. That's all."

Jo didn't go. She wanted to say something. Tell him he'd been the most marvellous boss, that it had all been fun. That he'd made her life for her. "Lady Reith rang up, Sir John. She's coming to collect you at six," was all she said.

"Oh, I'd forgotten. That wretched party at the Cromers."

Jo went out hurriedly. She said nothing to Sylvia the typist. She typed out the letter she'd just taken down. She didn't make one mistake. Later she'd take it down to the copying machine. It was half-past-five. Sylvia went home.

Just before six her phone went. It was the Chairman. The Board would like to see Sir John, if he didn't mind. She thought it odd that Ronald Norman hadn't spoken to the Director General himself. She knocked on the office door. "The Board will see you now, Sir John."

"Thank you, Miss Stanley."

John walked past her and along the corridor to the Board Room. He was no longer sorry for himself. He was angry. An anger white hot, but controlled. Anger with the cowardly men who sat as Governors, the cowardly Chairman, the Prime Minister and all the other feeble yes men who were committing this monstrous injustice. And anger with himself for letting them.

He came into the Board Room. The men of clay looked at him, half smiling—warily watching. He didn't wait for their explanations. "I have come to inform the Board that I no longer wish my name to be put forward to the Prime Minister as a candidate for the next Chairmanship. I do not even wish to have any further connection whatsoever with the British Broadcasting Corporation."

It was almost worth it just to see their sycophantic smiles leave their faces in dust and ashes.

Norman was the first to recover. "You mean you're resigning officially . . . I see." His years of training failed to produce a parallel situation. He thumbed through his papers, as though hoping there'd be a section on "Resignations—unexpected . . . "Er, thank you, Sir John . . . Well, may I accept your resignation on behalf of the B.B.C. And um . . . and . . . may I say that I do so with sorrow and gratitude for all the work you've . . ."

"There's no need for you to fumble for platitudes." He turned on the others. "No farewell speeches, please. And no farewell presentations paid for out of B.B.C. funds."

"If that's how you wish it to be, Sir John." said Norman.

"I do."

"Well . . ." said Norman, almost with relief and turning to more pleasant matters. "We've just agreed, you'll be pleased to hear, that you should receive a year's salary in advance."

"Even though you're not entitled to it," Sir Ian Fraser stabbed at him out of the darkness.

"Not entitled, Sir Ian?" John's scorn was allowed to pour out. "So the Director General is not entitled to the same treatment as any other member of the staff when leaving?"

"Strictly speaking, no. After all, you made the rules."

"Then I shall abide by the rules. I do not wish for ten thousand pounds and will refuse it if offered."

He marched to the door.

"Think it over, John." Norman was genuinely sorry. "I say . . . we all say . . ."

"You've said enough."

He left the hated Board Room for the last time, and strode back down the corridor.

Muriel was in the main office. She was with Jo Stanley. John saw at once that she knew. "Hullo, Musie," he said, and went straight past her into his office.

Muriel followed him after a moment. He was on the telephone. "Is Sir Noel Ashbridge there? . . . Well, get him." He looked across at Muriel. She seemed almost plaintiff in her desire to be of help, but saying nothing. "They don't want me, Musie. I shall start at Imperial Airways on Monday. At least I shan't have to sit through any more of their interminable Board Meetings. They can speak peace to each other *ad infinitum* for all I care."

Ashbridge came on the phone. "Ashbridge? I have one television set and one wireless at home. Arrange for them to be removed tomorrow." Ashbridge protested. "There's nothing wrong with them except that they are the property of the B.B.C."

"John, dearest . . ." Muriel moved towards him.

"Oh, Ashbridge. I want to give you something. I would have given it to Peter Eckersley, but he's not here and you're the next best thing." Muriel was amazed that he was chatting away as though nothing had happened. "Yes, he used to joke about it being a certificate for regular attendance at Sunday School. It hangs above my desk. It belonged to my father—it was given to him by the teacher he admired most . . . When he passed in Natural Philosophy at Aberdeen . . . I know that you'll appreciate the fact that it's signed by your hero—the man who discovered wireless if any man did—Clerk Maxwell. I'll give it to Miss Stanley to give to you." He put the phone down and carefully removed the certificate from the wall. Muriel watched him. He was clearing his office.

Norman came in. "Hullo, Muriel." He looked deeply concerned. "John, I hope you'll reconsider the money. After all, it's yours by right—and you've got a family to think about."

John stared right through him, but he stood his ground. "But there's one more thing . . . The Board's asked me if you wouldn't mind putting your resignation . . . in writing." He still faced John's look of contempt. He had a duty to perform. He was the jailer with the death warrant. "In writing . . . for tidiness sake."

"For tidiness sake, then." Mockery and contempt. John sat down at his desk, carefully took out a piece of writing paper, removed his fountain pen from his pocket, unscrewed the top and started to write—very deliberately.

Norman went on. "We all feel terrible you should go like this, John. Everybody will want to give you a proper send-off. Not just the governors—everybody. It's a personal loss . . . especially for me."

Muriel felt sorry for the poor man. John would spare him nothing. "But you need my resignation in writing. Once you've announced your betrothal to the attractive suitor of your choice, you don't want to wake up in the morning and find a dissolute old wretch on the doorstep, claiming restitution of his rights. Now then . . ." He started to write again. "I resign . . . I shall resign . . . I have resigned. There it is in all three tenses. Best wishes, Yours Sincerely, J.C.W. Reith." He smiled at Norman, then added two words. "Late B.B.C."

He blotted the paper carefully and held it out at arm's length.

Norman took it. "Thank you." He could not go like this. "I feel it's my fault somehow. I feel I could have saved you this humiliation."

"I hear you, man—is that understood? . . . I hear you very well!"

Norman left sadly, but gladly.

John continued to take down the things he valued. Doubtless

he'd be coming back to work during the weeks to come, but the
job was no longer his, the office was no longer his. He packed
his tents like an Arab and would steal away in the night. He
placed the photographs of his father and mother in his briefcase.
Muriel helped him on with his coat. He picked up the certificate
for Ashbridge and looked round his office. *His* office for the last
time.

He paused a moment by Miss Stanley's desk, and put the
certificate in front of her. Muriel followed him out.

In the main hall, John only lingered long enough to shake
hands with Kilroy. There was nothing to be said. It was all there
to be seen.

Plater held the door open for them. Muriel suddenly turned
back to Kilroy and kissed him on the cheek.

Kilroy and Plater and a few members of the B.B.C. staff who
knew nothing of what was going on, watched John and Muriel
leave the B.B.C.

He wrote in his diary: "No farewell ceremony. I walked out as
quietly as I had walked in . . . First Director General of the British
Broadcasting Corporation . . . John Charles Walsham Reith . . .
and that's the end of that!"

Epilogue

As long ago as 1915, John had written to his father that he'd be in the Cabinet in ten years. In 1940 he got there—Chamberlain's reward for clearing up British Airways! Baldwin promptly wrote to the new Minister of Information, "Patience first and last and all the way. Be yourself always", in block letters above his own address. John wasn't quite sure for whom the advice was intended, but it was advice John couldn't possibly take. If he were "patient first and last and all the way" he wouldn't be John Reith.

After Chamberlain resigned, John poured his energies into the Ministry of Transport and then the Ministry of Works. For a short time he thought he and Churchill were friends, but gradually he tired of his unnatural role playing second fiddle. Neither man quarrelled in public, both recognised the other's gifts, but Churchill went round making jokes about "that great Wuthering Height" and John behaved with his customary lack of tact, openly complaining to anyone within hearing distance that he couldn't bear sitting through meetings: "Winston shows off all the time, and feeds on the laughter of his sycophantic ministers."

When he eventually got the sack, it should have been no surprise. But John was, as ever, oblivious to the sensibilities of others. He blamed everyone but himself. His desire to nationalise transport was hardly likely to endear him to the Conservative Party, but that was not the reason for his own sudden transport to the Upper House. The letters exchanged between the two "great men" tell the whole story of John's success and failure as a politician. That he still hoped to be made use of is clear from his

refusal to become Lord High Commissioner of the Church
Assembly of Scotland—the sop Churchill threw in his direction.

Personal and Private   The Athenaeum
                                                           Pall Mall, SW1

                                                           January 1st 1946

   This letter I have wanted to write to you for more than two years.
There is nothing you can do about it now, but I felt I must send it.
   When Mr Chamberlain asked me to become Minister of Information, that office and ministry were in notorious disrepute, without
terms of reference or authority; but I imagined it was my duty to do
as bid. In addition to giving up an assured contractual position till I
was 60, and dropping to a third of my income, I surrendered the
right to £38,000 I could then have claimed. I (and my family) have
had reason to regret that.
   When I paid my first ministerial call on you, you said you knew
me chiefly as the one who had kept you from broadcasting on India.
In fact it was a Board decision, and after meeting the then chairman
you said to me 'I can see you're a friend'. I was. And after reading
your *World Crisis* I wrote that I would have given anything to have
worked direct to you in war. That was my attitude when you became
Prime Minister.
   After four months in Transport you asked me to go to the Lords
and take over the new Works Ministry. I did not want to leave the
Commons; was this an order? 'Yes', you replied, 'I command you to'.
I never heard it suggested that I had not done what you put me to
do in either Works or Planning; nor have subsequent events so
pointed.
   You can have no idea of the utter shock of your dismissal letter of
21.2.42. You wrote that I had served you loyally and well. I had; and
was only anxious for greater opportunity so to do; but I was not a
member of the Conservative Party, and I think I know what
happened.
   My reply pleased you, and when I declined the Lord High
Commissionership, 'being passionately anxious to contribute to the
war effort to the utmost of my power', you understood. I thought
you would soon enable me to do so.
   After waiting three months I joined the Navy, hoping at least to be
busy and fill in the time of waiting. I am glad I did not know I would
still be waiting at the end of the war.

A year later you wrote 'You may be sure I will try my best to find suitable employment for your well-known energy and capacity . . . it would be a great pleasure to me that you were pulling your full weight in the war'. That was in March 1943.

I am proud of my Admiralty work, and it takes skill to crack nuts with a steam hammer—anyhow for one of my temperament. And I doubt if a day passed that I did not hope for the word from you that never came.

Incidentally I could not but note that others dismissed had, or were given, sufficient alternative employment and income, or were otherwise recompensed. There was nothing for me.

I was taken from the Admiralty at the end of last year and did a record Empire tour, bringing back a better agreement on tele-communications than anyone had expected, especially in view of the difficult situation which had developed before I went. On return I made preparations for an imperial conference and took the chair at it. I do not think it could have been better prepared for or more successful. But I was still hoping to hear from you.

I have (like you) a war mentality and other qualities which should have commended themselves to you. Even in office I was nothing like fully stretched; and I was completely out of touch with you. You could have used me in a way and to an extent you never realised. Instead of that there has been the sterility, humiliation and distress of all these years—'eyeless in Gaza'—without even the consolation Samson had in knowing it was his own fault. And that is how and where I still am.

Intimating receipt of Reith's note, Churchill's reply came by telegram and then by letter.

WESTERN 1617

On board/R.M.S. QUEEN ELIZABETH.
28 HYDE PARK GATE,
LONDON, S.W.7.

January 11, 1946.

My dear Lord Reith,

I am grieved to receive your letter of January 1 although I am glad you wrote it. I know what a sacrifice you made when you gave up your position with British Airways in order to join Mr. Chamberlain's Government, and I thought you would have been fully justified in stipulating that a certain financial provision should be made for you, as has been done in other not dissimilar cases.

So far as my Administration is concerned, I have always admired your abilities and energy, and it was with regret that I was not able to include you in the considerable reconstruction of the Government in February, 1942. This was a time of great stress, when I was unable to provide for several able Ministers. Several times since then I have considered you for various posts which became vacant, but I always encountered considerable opposition from one quarter or another on the ground that you were difficult to work with. This was particularly so when, if my memory serves me right, I raised the question of your becoming again the Head of British Airways. My task in making political appointments in a Coalition Government, where certain balances had to be preserved, was hard, and I have no doubt that under the extreme pressure of war events I often made mistakes. I am unfeignedly sorry for the pain which you felt which I understand very fully, as I was myself, for eleven years, out of office before the war, during the last six of which I earnestly desired to take part in the work of preparation.

I admired the courage and efficiency with which you made yourself a place and a reputation in the Admiralty and you were still often in my mind as a candidate for high employment up till the time when I was myself suddenly and unexpectedly dismissed from office by the workings of our political system.

If you think I can be of service to you at any time, pray let me know; for I am very sorry that the fortunes of war should have proved so adverse to you, and I feel the State is in your debt.

Believe me,
Yours sincerely,
Winston S. Churchill

That was the end of the matter for Churchill. But John added it to the collection of injuries which festered within him. He'd read Huxley's *Eyeless in Gaza* years before and dubbed it "disgusting, but well written". Now he became disgusted with himself and everyone else.

When war broke out he'd been in the United States with Muriel and the children. He could easily have left them safely there. Instead he remarked with Shakespearean vigour, "By the Almighty, I would rather have my children suffer the bombing in England, than pass the dangers away from it while others are suffering." He had come back to save the nation. He stuck a carefully cut out picture of Hitler in his scrapbook, and prepared for the coming conflict. The following pages contained no call to arms. The Minister of Works had no Ambassadors and Presidents knocking at his door, only delegates from the "Allotment Association", anxious to know what he planned for them after the war.

Once more he was "sick at heart". Then came Churchill's curt note of dismissal. After a week or two of total shock, he sought out an admiral, and got himself signed on as a very junior naval officer. His salary dropped from £10,000 a year to £1.7.2d a day—though he got £45 towards the cost of his uniform. He liked the life, rather as he'd enjoyed being mistaken for his own butler while taking navigation classes five years earlier. He felt akin to Lawrence of Arabia alias Aircraftman Ross—except that he was alias Lieutenant Commander the Lord Reith. He'd got on well with Lawrence who'd given him his Arab shirt for use at fancy dress parties. The scrapbook soon began to fill with naval orders and when he was promoted to Captain and became responsible for the design and supply of coastal craft, the scrapbook bulged with interminable reports. He certainly "cracked nuts with a steam hammer".

He saw little of his family, though he wrote urgently to Sir John Anderson, pointing out that keeping Harrias House going on £350 was beyond his means, and suggesting he be given a cottage on the Astors' estate. Meanwhile he was organising "Operation Neptune", and enjoying the march towards victory.

Churchill was pushed out at his utmost of triumphs and the new Labour Government forgot their dislike of the erstwhile anti-trade unionist Director General. John flew off round the world to reorganise the telecommunications of the Empire. He revelled in travel: 15,000 miles in ten days. Then followed two years of "stagnation in the Lords", chairing planning committees. "The government's planning policy still stands, and is standing still" was one of his rare jokes in the Lords. The outcome of all this was the plan for Greater London and the arrival on the map of such places as Hemel Hempstead. True to his self disgust, he felt no sense of achievement from his labours.

At last, in 1951, the colossus was reawakened. He took over

the hopelessly disorganised and wasteful "Overseas Development Corporation". Millions had been poured down the African
drains. Within a year, John had visited nearly all the countries
concerned and established the O.D.C. as a vital force in colonial
development. He was back in his own class, with people like Sir
Roy Walensky bemoaning that if only he'd been appointed
Governor General, the Rhodesian Federation could have been
saved.

After eight years he was once more cut down. Lennox Boyd
summoned him to his office, and said that after eight and a half
years as Chairman, John would have to go. John asked: "You
mean I'm past being Chairman?" He got neither yes nor no for
an answer. He walked out and the wheel turned again. It was six
years before John cold be persuaded to set foot in the building
again. History repeats itself.

When Sir William Haley had become Director General, after
the Second World War, he had worked very hard to heal the
breach between the B.B.C. and its founder. John came to
mistrust him in the end because he failed to stand up to the
Government over the introduction of commercial television. "He
should have resigned in protest." But he pasted Haley's letter in
his scrapbook nevertheless.

> This generation is seeing more and more clearly the boon your
> vision conferred on them. Your conception of what broadcasting
> should do was one of the great sociological and educational acts of
> all time. This sense is most alive in the place where it is most valued,
> in the B.B.C. itself. This great organisation is not only proud of its
> founder; it reaches back and strives forward, to the strength and
> truth of your traditions. The feeling is not confined to your old
> colleagues. It is the driving force of the great body of us who never
> had the privilege of working with you. In the long years which
> have gone by since you left, those traditions have never been
> destroyed. At times they may have been dormant, today they are
> awake again, and if the B.B.C. does not house John Reith in body, it
> does in spirit.

In 1947 John had once again set foot in the B.B.C. The "Reith
Lectures" were to be inaugurated. He was given red carpet

treatment, escorted up to his old office by the Director General.
He wrote:

> I used to dream so often that I was back at the B.B.C. It was all so
> vivid. But when I returned there in reality—returned to my own
> office of yesteryear—I didn't even know where I was. I regretted that
> I had yielded to their blandishments. I wished profoundly I had
> never gone back. They put the 'Distinguished Visitors Book' on the
> desk in front of me, and put a pen in my hand. I reflected that I had
> appended various titles to my signature . . . Mayor, Captain R.N.V.R.,
> Minister of the Crown, Chairman, Director General, Knight of the
> Thistle, Peer of the Realm, Lord High Commissioner and Queen's
> Representative. . . . But none had given me such satisfaction as when
> I first signed over a rubber stamp in a foundry stores shed at Larbert
> "Transport Officer. Lieutenant 5th Scottish Rifles." My first real
> job, my first real title. I was a somebody, an object of mystification,
> envy and respect. It was expedient to be on friendly terms with
> me—I could perform or withold services. I was a power in the
> land—magnificent—like the Gold Star. John Charles Walsham Reith.

In a sense, nothing more happened to John. He became
Chairman of British Oxygen and toured the company's overseas
plants with his secretary. He saw his children married, but
refused to attend Marista's wedding reception and always
referred to her husband as Mr Leishman. John did remain
devoted to Muriel and she to him. He was Rector of Glasgow
University and had a grace and favour lodging in Holyrood
House. He died rich in honours but poor in money—his moral
principles intact to the end.

Select Bibliography

Andrew Boyle, *Only The Wind Will Listen,* Hutchinson, London, 1972

Asa Briggs, *The History of Broadcasting in the United Kingdom,* Oxford University Press, London, 1965, volumes 1-111

BBC Archives (Reith)

A.R. Burrows, *The Story of Broadcasting,* Cassell, London, 1924

Peter Eckersley, *The Power Behind the Mike,* Cape, London, 1941

Maurice Gorham, *Sound and Fury,* Percival Marshall, London, 1948

Mary Agnes Hamilton, *Remembering My Old Friends,* Jonathan Cape, London, 1944

R.S. Lambert, *Ariel and All His Quality,* Gollancz, London, 1940

J.C.W. Reith, *Into the Wind,* Hodder & Stoughton, London, 1949

John Reith, *Wearing Spurs,* Hutchinson, London, 1966

Index

248, 254, 259, 260, 261
Noyelles 149
Nuremberg Rally 222

Odhams, Christopher 146
Edward 37, 39, 45, 46, 62, 150
John 39, 150, 179
Lottie 62
Mr 40, 46, 62, 127
Mrs 30, 32, 36, 37, 38, 39, 40, 45, 46,
48, 61, 62, 158
Muriel 7, 8, 10, 15, 18, 20, 21, 22, 23,
24, 25, 26, 27, 28, 29, 30, 31, 32,
33, 34, 35, 36, 37, 38, 39, 40, 41,
43, 44, 45, 46, 48, 49, 50, 51, 52,
55, 56, 58, 59, 60, 62, 63, (m. John
Reith) 64
Press 39, 109, 110, 126, 175
Sylvia 120, 121
William 62, 77, 79, 109, 119, 126,
141, 175
Oglivie, Professor 239, 254
Orpheus Choir 191

Paderewski 182
Palmer, Rex 90, 92, 94
Pavlova 60
Payne, Tom 88, 89
Peacock 209
Pease, Mr 104, 105, 106
Peg Leg Pete 189
Philips, Doris 141, 175, 178
Plater 142, 193, 262
Post Master General 121, 137, 138,
143, 190, 191, 196, 207, 216, 217, 224
Price, Harry 206

Queen Anne's Mansions 97
Queen Mary 194
Radio Times 109, 203
Radio Unions Conference·165
Reith, Ada (Mother) 5, 8, 11, 12, 31,
37, 39, 41, 43, 44, 54, 55, 62, 63,
67, 75, 79, 82, 97, 98, 99, 100, 101,
111, 112, 116, 119, 120, 121, 122,
129, 130, 132, 139, 140, 142, 149,

150, 197, 198, 203, 204, 258
Archie 37, 45, 62, 67, 83, 199
Beth 17, 37, 45, 70, 83, 161
Christopher 164, 176, 187, 188, 203,
204, 215, 216, 217, 241, 242, 243,
244, 249
Douglas 15, 45, 51, 54, 55, 59, 60,
62, 63, 67, 78, 110, 114, 199
Ernest 199
George (Father) 5, 8, 11, 12, 25, 27,
31, 36, 37, 40, 41, 42, 44, 70, 75,
76, 80, 81, 82, 94, 98, 122, 147,
197, 198
Jean 5, 11, 37, 40, 41, 43, 44, 54, 55,
62, 67, 98, 99, 100, 101, 110, 111,
114, 119, 120, 122, 129, 130, 140,
150, 179, 187, 197, 198, 199, 230
John, early days 5-22, courtship of
Muriel Odhams 23-34, proposal
35-6, engagement 36-62, news of
father's stroke 36, father's death
42, demob 40, General Manager
of Beardmore's 44-74, marriage
63, honeymoon 65-6, jealousy of
Maisie Henderson 68-9, resignation from Beardmore's 74, Sir
William Bull 79-80, BBC 84-262,
General Strike 119-34,
Knighthood 136, Visit to France
146-50, birth of son 158, Berlin
171-80, USA 183-4, robbery 187,
daughter 191, mother's death
198-200, Imperial Airways 256,
requested by Govt. to leave BBC
257, resignation 259-62
Marista 203, 204, 215, 216, 217, 242,
249, 251, 253
Muriel (née Odhams) 65, 67, 69, 70,
71, 72, 74, 75, 76, 77, 78, 79, 83,
86, 87, 88, 90, 97, 98, 99, 100, 101,
102, 109, 110, 112, 114, 115, 116,
118, 119, 120, 121, 126, 127, 128,
129, 130, 132, 133, 135, 137, 138,
139, 140, 141, 142, 144, 146, 147,
148, 149, 150, 152, 153, 154, 156,
157, 158, 159, 160, 163, 164, 165,